cal-

/20

D1585327

METHUEN'S MANUALS OF MODERN PSYCHOLOGY

EDITED BY C. A. MACE

# IMPRINTING
## AND EARLY LEARNING

# IMPRINTING
## AND EARLY LEARNING

### W. SLUCKIN

*Reader in Psychology*
*University of Leicester*

## METHUEN & CO LTD
11 NEW FETTER LANE · LONDON EC4

*First published in* 1964

© *W. Sluckin*, 1964

*Printed in Great Britain by*
*Spottiswoode, Ballantyne & Co. Ltd.*
*London & Colchester*

To Tim and Andy

# ACKNOWLEDGMENTS

I was initially encouraged to write this book by my wife, Alice, by Vida Carver, and by Professor C. A. Mace. I profited greatly from many discussions with my friends Eric Salzen and Keith Taylor and with Professor Gillmore Lee. I should like to thank Professor Drever for suggesting the use of the phrase 'exposure learning'. I am most grateful for the constructive criticisms I have had from all those who so kindly read the draft typescript—my friends, Douglas Graham, Gillmore Lee, Keith Taylor and Robert Thomson—and also my wife and Professor Mace; needless to say, they are not responsible for the faults that remain. I wish to acknowledge the permission of Drs G. Gottlieb, E. H. Hess, H. James, H. Moltz and E. A. Salzen to reproduce diagrams.

W. S.

# CONTENTS

# PREFACE

Rapid learning of a characteristic type observed in young goslings, ducklings, chicks, etc., which is known as imprinting, has in recent years attracted much interest. This has been in no small measure the result of the admirable writings of Konrad Lorenz. The continued interest in this field of research has been bound up with the realisation among students of behaviour that imprinting and imprinting-like processes may be highly significant in the ontogenetic development of very many species, possibly including our own. The study of imprinting has become an area of collaboration between zoologists, who were the initiators of the research, and psychologists, who promptly took it up and extended it. The early work consisted of 'field' observations and experiments, mostly on the Continent of Europe. Later on, laboratory studies under stricter environmental controls were begun, mostly in America and in this country.

Perhaps the first to stress the theoretical importance of imprinting for understanding the mechanisms of instinct and learning was W. H. Thorpe. Then, at Cambridge, Hinde, Thorpe and Vince conducted their pioneering investigations of imprinting in young moorhens and coots. Subsequently, experimental studies were started in Edinburgh, Durham, Liverpool, Leicester and elsewhere. My own interest in imprinting was stimulated by the early Cambridge work; since then I have worked in this field at the Universities of Durham and Leicester. This book is a progress report – as indeed any report on a rapidly developing branch of science must be; it can be anticipated that during the next few years many further experimental studies of imprinting will be published in the technical journals.

I have attempted in this book, first, to trace the history of the interest in imprinting and similar processes, and to consider imprinting side by side with certain related concepts and empirical studies. Second, I have tried to review the full range of experiments which throw light on the characteristic nature of imprinting. Third, I have set out to consider imprinting in relation to conditioning, and especially, to early learning. Finally, I have allowed myself to 'think aloud' about the broader implications of imprinting, tentatively pointing to the bearing of the facts and theories of imprinting upon educational, social and abnormal psychology.

*Leicester, January* 1964                          WLADYSLAW SLUCKIN

# Chapter 1

# A HISTORICAL INTRODUCTION

The young of many species stay for a time with their begetters; if they did not, their survival would be imperilled. The close proximity of parents and offspring is brought about in part by parental care and in part by an affiliation tendency in the young. In many species, including man, the neonate is largely helpless, requiring care or nursing. In such *altricial* species, as they are called, the tie between the parents and their offspring is necessarily due less to the activity of the young than to the activity of the adults. In non-altricial species, sometimes called *precocial*, infant individuals possess well-developed sense organs, are capable of locomotion, and themselves contribute substantially to the establishment of the bonds between them and their parents.

In this category are the young of ungulates, such as lambs, kids and calves, as well as the young of some other mammalian species. Among birds, fledgelings of the so-called nidifugous species, mostly ground-nesting, can run or swim very soon after hatching. Such young birds – domestic chicks, ducklings and goslings, to name a few – tend to follow their parents almost as soon as they are out of the egg. The initial tendency in the young to cling to, or to follow, parent-figures may be described as instinctive or innate, by which is meant that the young are not trained and do not have to learn to behave in this filial manner.

Approach and following on the part of the new-born or newly hatched creature are responses to stimulation. What is it, then, that evokes these responses in the agile neonate, and under what conditions? Some early systematic observations were reported by D. A. Spalding in 1873, who coupled his interesting observations with some venturesome speculations about the nature of instinct. Spalding's studies were brought to the notice of the present generation by

Professor J. B. S. Haldane, who arranged for the paper by Spalding, called 'Instinct, with Original Observations on Young Animals', to be reprinted in full in 1954 in the *British Journal of Animal Behaviour*. While considering some 'manifestations of instinct', Spalding (1873) wrote as follows:

> Chickens as soon as they are able to walk will follow any moving object. And, when guided by sight alone, they seem to have no more disposition to follow a hen than to follow a duck, or a human being.

Spalding was concerned to establish that certain features of the behaviour of chicks, including the following of moving objects, were instinctive rather than learned. To this end he devised an ingenious procedure whereby newly hatched chicks were largely deprived of visual experiences so that they could scarcely learn anything about their visual environment. To exclude the possibility that the eye 'may have had opportunities of being educated', Spalding 'had recourse to the following expedient'.

> Taking eggs just when the little prisoners had begun to break their way out, I removed a piece of the shell, and before they had opened their eyes drew over their heads little hoods, which, being furnished with an elastic thread at the lower end, fitted close round their necks. The material of the hoods was in some cases such as to keep the wearers in total darkness; in other instances it was semi-transparent.

The experimental procedure, in Spalding's own words, was as follows.

> In this state of blindness – the blindness was very manifest – I allowed them to remain from one to three days. The conditions under which these little victims of human curiosity were first permitted to see the light were often carefully prepared.

Spalding then observed the behaviour of his chicks after unhooding them. From his observations he concluded that pecking, entailing the ability to perceive direction and distance, was an instinctive act rather than a learned skill. With regard to the tendency to follow moving objects these were Spalding's remarks:

> The unacquired power of following by sight was exemplified in the case of a chicken that, after being unhooded, sat complaining and motionless for six minutes, when I placed my hand on it for a few seconds. On removing my hand the chicken immediately followed it by sight backward and forward and all round the table.

Another chick 'was unhooded when nearly three days old'. This chick was placed about half-an-hour later 'within sight and call of a hen with a brood of its own age'. 'After standing chirping for about a minute, it started off towards the hen . . .'.

So much for the conditions of following. Spalding also had something to say about the circumstances in which following will not occur. 'Something curious' – he reported –

came to light in the case of three chickens that I kept hooded until nearly four days old – a longer time than any I have yet spoken of. Each of these on being unhooded evinced the greatest terror of me, dashing off in the opposite direction whenever I sought to approach it. The table on which they were unhooded stood before a window, and each in its turn beat against the glass like a wild bird. One of them darted behind some books, and squeezing itself into a corner, remained cowering for a length of time. We might guess at the meaning of this strange and exceptional wildness; but the odd fact is enough for my present purpose. Whatever might have been the meaning of this marked change in their mental constitution – had they been unhooded on the previous day they would have run to me instead of from me – it could not have been the effect of experience; it must have resulted wholly from changes in their own organization.

Some years later, referring to Spalding's work, William James (1890) asserted in his *Principles of Psychology, Vol. II, Ch.* 24, that 'These little creatures show opposite instincts of attachment and fear, either of which may be aroused by the same object, man'. James could have said, to render Spaldings' view faithfully, that the tendencies to approach or fear might be aroused by any moving object, according to the time of the chick's first confrontation with that object. For Spalding appears to have suggested that, as a rule, chicks up to about three days of age will approach and follow the first moving object seen, but at about four days of age the first moving object encountered will be avoided rather than approached. It is open to doubt whether this could be generally true, considering the striking individual differences in behaviour among chicks (see Chapter 3), and the very small number of subjects actually observed by Spalding. Nevertheless, the view that timidity gradually develops in the very young animal, and that it eventually overcomes or inhibits the tendency to approach and follow moving objects, might be substantially true.

It is interesting to note that many years after Spalding's observations and James's remarks, Fabricius (1951a), studying in Finland the behaviour of several different species of wild duck, observed likewise that the very same moving objects that would be approached and followed by his ducklings were also capable at other times or in other circumstances of evoking fear in them. Later, Ramsay and Hess (1954) confirmed this; and Hinde, Thorpe and Vince (1956) found that objects which elicit following in moorhens and coots may also elicit fear in these birds; cf. Hinde (1961). How following and fear are related is a challenging problem. Experimental studies bearing on its solution are surveyed and discussed later, in Chapter 7.

It appeared to Spalding that the chick would follow its mother provided it had the opportunity to do so while it was young enough. If confronted for the first time with its mother when the opportune time had passed, the chick would be quite indifferent to her. Spalding gives the following account of the behaviour of a chicken that was first confronted with its mother at ten days of age.

The hen followed it, and tried to entice it in every way; still it continually left her and ran to the house or to any person of whom it caught sight. This it persisted in doing, though beaten back with a small branch dozens of times, and indeed cruelly maltreated. It was also placed under the mother at night, but it again left her in the morning.

The implication of such observations could simply be that an instinctive act can occur at some periods of the animal's life but not at others. There may be a special time for the display of each innate tendency. At an early age the chick approaches and follows moving objects. Later, it flees from moving objects. Very much later the fowl displays sexual behaviour. Likewise young mammals cling to their mothers while very young, play at a later stage, and so on. However, a more important conclusion to be drawn from Spalding's observations could be that there is in the life of an animal a critical period for acquiring or learning certain kinds of behaviour. If during such a critical period the chick did not experience the proximity of its mother, then the chick could never subsequently develop a lasting attachment to her. More generally, certain forms of behaviour must be acquired during the critical period, or they will not be acquired at all.

William James (1890) in his *Principles of Psychology, Vol. II, Ch.* 24, refers to 'the inhibition of instincts by habits' and to what he calls the 'law of transitoriness'. The latter states that 'Many instincts ripen at a certain age and then fade away'. He develops this as follows:

... during the time of such an instinct's vivacity, objects adequate to arouse it are met with, a *habit* of acting on them is formed, which remains when the original instinct has passed away; but that if no such objects are met with, then no habit will be formed; and, later on in life, when the animal meets the objects, he will altogether fail to react, as at the earlier epoch he would instinctively have done.

James then refers specifically to the tendency to follow and to the lasting ties to the objects of following. He writes:

In the chickens and calves, ... it is obvious that the instinct to follow and become attached fades out after a few days, and that the instinct of flight then takes its place, the conduct of the creature toward man being decided by the formation or non-formation of a certain habit during those days.

James suggests that the behaviour involving following, and thereby becoming attached to the thing followed, is at once innate and acquired. This combination of instinct and learning is the interesting feature of the development of following in an animal such as the domestic chicken. Now, many types of behaviour are purely innate and need not be learned at all. Equally, many kinds of behaviour are characteristically acquired or learned. Developing an attachment through following, as Spalding and James have described it, combines the instinctive and acquired factors; for following is instinctive, but the attachment to, or the preference for, a particular class of objects is acquired. This type of behaviour has excited great interest in recent times: Thorpe (1956, 1963) in his book *Learning and Instinct in Animals* (see also Thorpe, 1951) judged this behaviour to be of 'rather exceptional theoretical interest'; the study of it, in Thorpe's view, promised to shed a good deal of light on the relationship of instinct to 'plastic processes in general'.

It would be perhaps misguided to build too much on the limited observations and theorising by Spalding and William James. In the first decade of this century fresh studies of the following response and the formation of attachments of young nidifugous birds were made by O. Heinroth in Germany. Heinroth read a paper in 1910 (published in 1911) about his work; and this paper received much publicity twenty-five years later when it was cited by the pioneer ethologist, Konrad Lorenz. Heinroth (1911) reported his studies of swans, geese and ducks from a variety of angles. Among other things, Heinroth found that incubator-hatched graylag goslings showed no fear when the incubator was opened and thereafter would follow people about. In Heinroth's own words:

> They look at you without betraying any sign of fear; and, if you handle them even briefly, you can hardly shake them off. They peep pitifully if you walk away, and soon follow you about religiously. I have known such a little creature to be content if it could just squat under the chair on which I sat, a few hours after I had taken it from the incubator! If you then take such a gosling to a goose family with young of the same age, the situation usually develops as follows. Goose and gander look suspiciously at the approaching person, and both try to get themselves and their young into the water as quickly as they can. If you walk towards them very rapidly, so that the young have no chance to escape, the parents, of course, put up a spirited defence. This is the time to place the small orphan among the brood and leave in a hurry. In the excitement, the parents at first regard the newcomer as their own, and show an inclination to defend it as soon as they see and hear it in human hands. But the worst is yet to come. It does not even occur to the young gosling to treat the two old birds as geese. It runs away, peeping loudly, and, if a human being happens to pass by, it follows him: it simply looks upon humans as its parents.

Thus, a gosling can become attached to a human being if, soon after hatching out, it encounters only human beings and not geese. This is not altogether surprising. Hens have often been used for incubating duck eggs; the ducklings that hatch from under a hen follow the hen around just as her own chicks do. Old folk tales tell us about the difficulties to which such mutual attachments of hen and ducklings may lead.

Lorenz (1935, 1937a) was impressed by the fact that a young bird does not instinctively recognise adult members of its own species. Its instinctive endowment merely predisposes it to follow the first moving thing it encounters – usually its mother, sometimes another member of its own species, occasionally a member of another species. But after having had some little experience of its mother, or of some other animal, or perhaps of a human being, the young animal forms a lasting attachment to the individual, or the class of individual, it has initially followed. We say that the young animal has become imprinted with, or imprinted to, this individual or this type of individual; and the phenomenon itself is known as imprinting. The word 'imprinting', used by Lorenz (1937b) in a paper which appeared in English, is a translation of the German word 'Prägung', used by Lorenz on other occasions (1935, 1937a).

It has been pointed out by Gray (1961a) that the term 'imprinting', or 'Prägung', used by Lorenz, and the 'einzuprägen', used earlier by Heinroth, have strong affinities to such well-known English phrases as 'to stamp in' or 'stamping in'. (Spalding himself – it may be noted – has used the phrase 'the stamp of experience'.) Gray thinks that Heinroth's ideas about instinct may have been influenced by the German eighteenth-century philosopher, Reimar (called in Latin, Reimarus), who is said to have contended that rapid early learning complements instinctive behaviour. Whatever Reimar's views may have been, he was not an observer of animal behaviour, and he probably knew nothing about the phenomenon of imprinting. This is apparent from the account of Reimar's writings by his French contemporary, the naturalist Leroy (see the English edition of Leroy's letters published in 1870 under the title 'The Intelligence and Perfectability of Animals from a Philosophic Point of View'), as also from the account by Brett in his 'History of Psychology' (cf. Brett, 1912 and 1921, and Peters (Ed.) 1953).

Now, Spalding observed the tendency in the newly hatched domestic chick to follow the first-seen moving object; and William James adumbrated the study of imprinting by noting that by following some objects early in life the animal 'forms a habit' of attachment to that class of objects. Lorenz went further: he specified, rather boldly, the characteristics of imprinting. Lorenz's writing is clear and vivid; and the present-day interest in imprinting, including its important implications in psychology, derives almost entirely from Lorenz's early observations of, and theorising about, this form of animal behaviour. Lorenz's early conception of imprinting was quite definitive; no wonder, therefore, that, as factual findings began to accumulate, this conception became the target of much severe criticism. But the later criticisms, fundamental and valid as they have been, only enhance Lorenz's very great initial contribution.

What then, precisely, were Lorenz's original views concerning imprinting? Lorenz (1935) wrote:

> The process of imprinting differs radically from the acquisition of the objects of other instinctive acts whose releasing mechanism is not innate. Whereas in the latter case the object seems always to be acquired by self-training, or learning, imprinting has a number of features which distinguish it fundamentally from a learning process. It has no equal in the psychology

of any other animal, least of all a mammal. However, I would point out certain analogies in human psychology, which appear in the form of pathological fixations on the object of an instinct.

First among the points that distinguish imprinting from ordinary learning is that the object acquisition in question can only take place within a brief critical period in the life of an individual. In other words, a very specific physiological state in the young animal's development is required to accomplish it.

Secondly, once the physiologically critical period is over, the animal knows the imprinted object of its innate reactions to a fellow member of the species exactly as though this knowledge were innate. It cannot be forgotten! Yet, as C. Bühler (1927) in particular points out, it is essential to anything learned that it can be forgotten! Of course, since our knowledge of this field is in its infancy, it is too early to claim definitely that the imprinting process is irreversible. I infer that it is so from a fact frequently observed in hand-raised birds. Once their instinctive social reactions are transposed to a human being, their behaviour does not change in the least even if they are later kept for years with other members of their own species and without human company.

To quote further Lorenz's own phrases, 'later behaviour is determined at a critical period', and 'this process of determination is irreversible'. It could, of course, be said that these features of the development of behaviour may be characteristic of all learning. In the first place, any acquired behaviour is sometimes acquired at some critical stage of the individual's life; for example, it appears that in learning a foreign language a true 'native accent' can be acquired only in childhood. Secondly, much ordinary learning is irreversible; the acquired ability to swim or to ride a bicycle is never really forgotten. However, in his earlier writings Lorenz stressed that imprinting had 'none of the essential earmarks of training'. Lorenz (1937a), in fact, wrote:

The animal does not act according to the principle of trial and error, as it does when acquiring an instinct-training interlocking, nor is it led by reward and punishment. Instead, an exposure to certain stimuli, very limited in time, determines its entire subsequent behaviour, without – and this is essential – this behaviour having necessarily been practised before the stimuli become effective. It is especially apparent in cases where considerable time elapses between the operation of the object-determining stimuli and the discharge of the instinctive act. Thus, as far as I have been able to observe, the object of the jackdaw's (*Coloeus monedula spermologus*) innate mating behaviour is already determined during the young bird's nesting period. Young jackdaws that are taken over by humans around the time they become fledged, will transfer the actions normally directed toward their parents to the humans; but it is too late to transpose their sexual behaviour. This cycle only shifts to a human if the animals are adopted much earlier. A musk drake (*Cairina moschata*) hatched with four siblings by a pair of grey geese, and led by them for seven weeks, subsequently proved to be bound to his siblings, that is, to his own species, in all his social activities. But when his mating reactions awoke the following year, they were focussed on the species of the foster parents, to whom he had paid no attention for over ten months.

In later years Lorenz's views underwent some evolution. Thus, twenty years after the publication of his famous paper 'Der Kumpan in der Umwelt des Vogels', Lorenz (1955), in a contribution to a symposium held in America, expressed the view that 'imprinting tapers off into learning', and that 'imprinting is definitely a type of conditioning'.

However, Lorenz's striking early views about imprinting stimulated a great deal of serious empirical research. Statements, like the one quoted below, were felt by students of behaviour to be a challenge to them. Lorenz (1937b) said:

... I wish to call the reader's attention more especially to the points in which this process differs from what we call associative learning. (1) The process is confined to a very definite period of individual life, a period which in many cases is of extremely short duration; the period during which the young partridge gets its reactions of following the parent birds conditioned to their object, lasts literally but a few hours, beginning when the chick is drying off and ending before it is able to stand. (2) The process, once accomplished, is totally irreversible, so that from then on, the reaction behaves exactly like an 'unconditioned' or purely instinctive response. This absolute rigidity is something we never find in behaviour acquired by associative learning, which can be unlearned or changed, at least to a certain extent.

The kind of evidence that is adduced for the seeming irreversibility of imprinting will be found in the earlier quotation in which Lorenz referred to a drake so indelibly imprinted to its foster-parents, geese, that it later directed its mating activities towards geese. Lorenz (1937b), contended that in earlier years Heinroth did not succeed in breeding hand-reared great-horned owls, ravens and other birds, because these tame birds had become imprinted to their human keepers instead of members of their own species, and consequently these birds would not court and mate with members of their own species. Now, there have been earlier reports of courtship activities of birds being directed towards individuals of species other than their own; Craig (1908) and Carr (1919) both quoted observations of birds made by Whitman, the American zoologist whose works were published posthumously under Carr's editorship; and there have been many later reports of sexual fixations in animals to inappropriate objects. All these reports are surveyed and discussed at some length in Chapter 4.

When Lorenz first described the phenomenon of imprinting in the mid-nineteen-thirties only a few facts were known about the conditions of occurrence of approach and following responses in infant animals and about the way that infant animals develop attachments, including sexual fixations, to the objects that they have earlier followed. Lorenz reported that, although Heinroth had previously succeeded in imprinting goslings, he himself found that incubator-hatched ducklings fled at the sight of man. Lorenz (1935) managed, however, by making quacking noises, to imprint mallard ducklings to himself. He achieved, in fact, in later years some fame among the wider public by crawling on all fours in front of a family of ducklings; cf. Lorenz (1952).

The first modern research studies primarily concerned with imprinting were conducted by Fabricius (1951a, b). Earlier, however, Cushing and Ramsay (1949) referred to imprinting in their investigations of non-inheritable factors of family unity in several nidifugous bird species: the quail, the turkey, the pheasant, the Muscovy duck, the domestic duck, and the domestic fowl. They observed the formation of various mixed families, each consisting of an adult female bird and a number of various young other than her own. Cushing and Ramsay concluded that family bonds in birds become established 'as a result of conditioning or imprinting acting at the time of hatching'.

Fabricius, however, went further in his investigations. Using such wild species of duck, as the shoveller, the tufted duck, and the eider duck he observed the 'approach reactions' of newly hatched ducklings to some sizable objects situated in an open space. He showed that wild ducklings could be quite readily imprinted to various moving objects. Fabricius's findings, concerning the different features of imprinting, are considered at some length in subsequent chapters. At a later date Fabricius conducted some further investigations of imprinting at the Wildfowl Trust Station at Slimbridge in Gloucestershire; cf. Fabricius and Boyd (1954) and Fabricius (1955). Before long, imprinting research was also begun at the Delta Waterfowl Research Station in Manitoba, Canada; see Nice (1953) and Collias and Collias (1956).

The researches just mentioned used wild species as subjects. An early systematic investigation of imprinting in young domestic birds – ducklings, chickens and turkey poults – was conducted in America by Ramsay (1951). Ramsay used domesticated Muscovy ducks and White Rock hens for rearing broods of chicks, turkey poults and ducklings. He also used a moving box and a football to evoke following in these young birds. Further laboratory experiments were conducted by Ramsay and Hess (1954). In these experiments mallard ducklings were imprinted to a model drake made to resemble as closely as possible a real mallard drake; much data concerning imprinting was collected under these conditions. From about that time on, more and more laboratory experiments on imprinting were started in different research centres.

A few years earlier Alley and Boyd (1950) set out to study in young coots not so much imprinting as such as the conditons of recognition by young coots of their parents. Alley and Boyd considered that the first stage of this learning consisted of learning to discriminate between the general characteristics of the species of coot and those of other moving creatures. They thought that the development of this ability was associated with the imprinting of young coots to their parents. However, these investigators also found that young coots would at the start almost as readily follow any moving object of suitable size, or approach the source of an artificial coot-like call. Alley and Boyd judged that young coots began to fear human beings only after becoming imprinted to adult coots, at about two days of age. It may be noted that this finding suggests that fear itself might be a *consequence* of imprinting. This is rather at variance with the view mentioned earlier – first implied by Spalding, and later made explicit by Hinde, Thorpe and Vince (1956) and others – that fear emerges in the course of maturation, independently of imprinting. However, the question of the relationship of fear to imprinting will be dealt with at length in Chapter 7.

If imprinting is the basis of recognition of members of their species by the young, then socialisation, or the tendency of members of the same species to flock together, may well have the same roots. This was the view put forward by Collias (1952); and it was later further elaborated by him (Collias, 1962). In point of fact some of the behaviour that Collias originally studied was the behaviour of individual domestic chicks, placed in a long runway, in response to the clucking which emerged from loud-speakers situated at one or the other of the two ends of the runway; as expected, naïve chicks responded to the clucking by approaching the source of the sound. This and related aspects of Collias's work are considered in Chapter 3. Here we need only mention that on the basis of various further investigations, Collias reached the conclusion that chicks become attached not only to the sound and sight of mother-hen but also to those of one another. This, thought Collias, was what happened in the normal course of events, and this was the first step towards the chicks' socialisation. In his view, the gregariousness of many animals starts with such initial social bonds, and is then greatly strengthened through associative learning. Imprinting as a socialising factor is considered at some length in Chapter 4.

In retrospect it appears that an important stage in the study of imprinting was reached about the year 1956. Several new research reports were published, e.g. Jaynes (1956), Klopfer (1956), and foremost among them, the detailed account by Hinde, Thorpe and Vince (1956) of their experiments with young coots and moorhens. These experiments were partly directed towards determining the character of the stimuli that evoked following. The conditions necessary for the establishment of following responses in young coots and moorhens were closely examined. Also, data were obtained concerning the sensitive period for imprinting. And a number of suggestions of a theoretical nature were made. The same year saw also the publication of *Learning and Instinct in Animals* by W. H. Thorpe (1956). Thorpe's book made a contribution to the study of imprinting in at least three ways. First, it surveyed previous reports of imprinting and similar phenomena in many different species. Second, it stressed the importance of imprinting in nature, and drew attention to the need for further research in this field. Third, it summarised and classified the knowledge of imprinting that had been gained up to the middle fifties.

Regarding the last point, it will be remembered that Lorenz's main publications about imprinting appeared shortly before the war, in 1935 and 1937. More than a decade later the characteristics of imprinting began to be seriously considered again by the Cambridge group of students of animal behaviour; cf. Thorpe (1951, 1955); Hinde (1955a, 1955b). Thorpe (1956), having considered the evidence then available, concluded that 'imprinting is peculiar in the following respects' (this statement remains unchanged in the 1963 edition of the book):

(1) The process is confined to a very definite and very brief period of the individual life, and possibly also to a particular set of environmental circumstances. (2) Once accomplished it is often very stable – in some cases perhaps totally irreversible. (3) It is often completed long before the various specific reactions to which the imprinted pattern will ultimately become linked are established. (4) It is supra-individual learning – a learning of the broad characteristics of the *species* – for if this were not so and the bird at this stage learnt (as it can easily do later) the individual characteristics of its companion, the biological effect would be frustrated.

Similar formulations of the characteristics of imprinting may also be found elsewhere; see, for example, Hinde (1959).

Originally, the term, imprinting, had been applied only to attachments rooted in the approach and following responses of goslings, ducklings, chickens and the like. Although imprinting may occur to specific sounds, as in the young of a hole-nesting species of duck, described by Klopfer (1959a, b), it usually is a visual attachment to some moving figure. Now, in view of the reports of seemingly similar behaviour of the young of various mammalian species, it has seemed reasonable to use the term, imprinting, more freely; cf. Hediger (1955), Thorpe (1956, 1963).

It is well known that lambs follow those who bring them up on the bottle. It is said that even after such animals have been weaned and have joined the flock, they approach the keeper and stay near him whenever given a chance. In cases of this kind, 'cupboard love' could be the main factor in the animals' attachment to people; but imprinting may not be altogether discounted. Grabowski (1941) described a case of the close devotion of a lamb to its human keeper. Scott (1945) reported that a lamb raised by himself and his wife on the bottle for the first few days of its life became very attached to people. Hediger (1955) quoted earlier reports of two young moufflons which followed the girl that looked after them. He also quoted cases of buffalo calves which, when separated from their mothers, followed the huntsmen's horses. A new-born zebra foal was said to have attached itself once to a moving car, running behind it and refusing to be chased away. There have also been reports of following responses in young red deer. More recently Altmann (1958) described a 'heeling' tendency, imprinting-like in character, in young moose calves. There are, too, reports by Hess (1959a) and by Shipley (1963) of imprinting in the domestic guinea pig.

In so far as imprinting is a special type of learning – rapid, lasting and not occasioned by such rewards as food or drink – certain other cases of learning may be regarded as more or less imprinting-like in character. Thorpe (1956, 1963) cites various examples of such learning in insects. One of the most striking is perhaps the case earlier described by Thorpe (1944) in some detail on the basis of previous reports: it is one of the young males of a particular species of grasshopper that can sing in 'rhythmic alternation', responding to artificially produced sounds of various frequencies; and adult males of this grasshopper sing in concert with their own kind, as if imprinted. Rather better understood, however, appears to be the learning of different songs by birds. The case that has been most rigorously investigated is that of the chaffinch. Collias and Joos (1953) described the acoustic spectrograph which permits a harmonic analysis of sounds, making it possible for bird songs to be analysed and compared with one another. With the aid of this instrument Thorpe (1954) found that the song of the chaffinch has 'a very restricted inborn basis'. The refinements of the song are learned. This imprinting-like, auditory learning appears to occur partly in the early weeks of the bird's life and partly during the bird's first spring. The variations of the chaffinch song found in different parts of the country appear to be due to this learning. However, different kinds of imprinting-like behaviour are considered more fully in Chapter 9.

Also in Chapter 9 we shall consider suggestions and speculations about imprinting in human beings. To what extent the study of imprinting has relevance to human behaviour is a controversial matter. This is considered in the last chapter, Chapter 10.

At this stage we may ask on what grounds certain kinds of acquired behaviour may be regarded as akin to imprinting, in the original Lorenzian sense of the term. In the first place learning by fledgelings in the course of following may, of course, be difficult to distinguish – as Hinde (1961) rightly stresses – from learning 'which occurs during feeding or brooding by the parent'. Secondly, imprinting-like learning in situations other than following may be as difficult, or more difficult, to distinguish from ordinary reward-learning. Acquired behaviour has been said to be imprinting-like whenever it has seemed to conform to the characteristics of imprinting, as specified, for example, by Thorpe (1956) and quoted earlier in this chapter.

However, a great many laboratory investigations of imprinting phenomena have been carried out in the later fifties and the sixties. Different features of imprinting have been examined and re-examined. As we shall see in the succeeding chapters, the reversibility, the critical period and many other features of imprinting appear less crucial now that they are better understood. While in some ways imprinting at the present time is seen to be much more like other forms of learning (e.g. Hinde, 1955a; Moltz, 1960; Sluckin and Salzen, 1961), in other ways the difference between imprinting-like learning and other learning is now clearer and sharper (e.g. Hess, 1959a; Sluckin and Salzen, 1961; Sluckin, 1962).

There is little that can be said by way of defining imprinting that cannot be challenged or queried. It would, however, be generally agreed that the term, in its empirical sense, refers to the formation by young precocial birds of relatively specific attachments. These develop from initial approach and following responses, and are not established by conventional conditioning employing such rewards as food and water (cf. Moltz, 1960, 1963). But, as we shall see in later chapters, approach and following are not crucial for imprinting. Attachment to any configuration of stimuli may be formed by the organism as a result of *exposure* to these stimuli. If so, then exposure to any sensory stimulation, leading to any kind of tie to this stimulation, may be said to be akin to imprinting phenomena. A statement such as this is too vague and too imprecise to serve as a sure means of distinguishing between behaviour acquired in an imprinting-like fashion and behaviour otherwise acquired. At the same time the references in this paragraph to imprinting in the initial and the extended senses will perhaps be useful in indicating the scope of our inquiry. In the next chapter we shall briefly consider some concepts and terms germane to imprinting; we shall then systematically review research findings and see what conclusions may be drawn from them.

# Chapter 2

# SOME CONCEPTS AND TERMS

Moving figures are but one of the many kinds of stimulation that may attract neonate individuals. Precocial birds also respond positively to certain noises, may be attracted by contact, and they seek, of course, warmth. Some new-born mammals approach moving objects; probably all respond to face-contact by head-turning; some react to the feel of certain textures by clasping the objects that provide it, and so on. An innately determined pattern of responses normally unites the neonate with its mother, or mother-substitute. And with time the attachments thus formed become more or less exclusive. As we have seen, the term, imprinting, initially referred to the formation of attachments built upon approach and following responses. However, there is no special reason why attachments which develop from other initial responses, for example, clasping and clinging, should not also be classed as imprinting.

It is quite clear that some kinds of stimulation attract, and others repel, the newly hatched or new-born young. The attractive or repellent quality of stimulation is inferred in the first place from the movements of the neonate. Approach and withdrawal are ultimately the only objective terms which indicate the motivational state of an animal (Schneirla, 1959). But different sounds made by animals are often coupled with their movements either towards or away from sources of stimulation. It is, therefore, often possible to judge the motivational state of an animal from the kind of noises it makes.

Consider, for instance, the domestic chicken. When lost, cold, or hungry, the chick emits characteristic, relatively loud cheeps descending in pitch, generally known as distress calls. When returned to the mother-figure, or to warmth, and a little later in life, when returned to food, the chick emits quieter, rather higher, rapid twittering notes, known to students of chick behaviour as pleasure or contentment calls. What is normally observed is that the chick tends to move away from objects or situations that evoke distress calls, and it tends to approach whatever stimulates contentment calls (see Collias, 1952, 1962). The two types of call made by the chick have been analysed spectrographically by Collias and Joos (1953); distinct to the ear, as they are, their records are even more distinct to the eye.

In nature the mother-hen provides the visual, the auditory and the tactual stimulation which attract chicks and elicit pleasure chirps from them. Warmth, too, comes from mother-hen, and food tends perhaps to be associated with her presence. But, as said previously, the chick becomes attached to mother-figure not primarily, or at all, because the figure satisfies the chick's physiological needs for warmth or nourishment. This is borne out by experiments, to be surveyed later, in which attachments were formed despite the conspicuous lack of anything in the objects of these attachments of any tangible physical value to the animal. In other words, imprinting does not depend on the presence of physiological rewards such as are used in conventional conditioning.

Now, infant rhesus monkeys make certain reflex responses to the stimulation provided by the mother-monkey, and clasping is probably the most significant of them. The infant-monkey's attachment to its mother may be said to develop from its initial innate responses to her (Harlow and Zimmermann, 1958, 1959; Harlow 1958, 1959, 1960, 1961, 1962). The baby-monkey's initial exposure to its mother ties it to her, much as the chick's early experiences tie it to the mother-hen.

New-born monkeys are suckled by their mothers. It would be in keeping with reinforcement-learning theory to suppose that the baby monkey's attachment to its mother develops as the baby learns to associate its mother's features with the relief from hunger and thirst which is provided by mother's milk. This supposition is testable, and it has been thoroughly tested by Harlow and his co-workers at Wisconsin.

These investigators separated the qualities of sensory stimulation supplied by a mother-monkey from the source of milk which the mother-monkey normally provides. In brief, two 'inanimate mother surrogates' were used, each a cylinder about the size of an adult monkey, placed at an angle to the floor. One cylinder was made of stiff wire mesh and was supplied with a lactating nipple; this was the 'wire mother'. The other cylinder was made of wood covered with soft cloth; this was the 'cloth mother'. The experimental infant monkeys were found to spend more time clinging to the cloth mother than with the milk-providing wire mother. Furthermore, the infants later showed unmistakable signs of attachment to the cloth mother and not to the wire mother. It was clear that the seeming affection for, and attachment to, the cloth mother that had grown in baby monkeys could not have been due to the physiological reward of the milk. The attachment appears to have developed simply as a result of the infant's early exposure and of his responses to the sensory stimulation which the cloth mother provided.

We shall see in Chapters 9 and 10 that human babies' affection for their mothers and attachment to them may also be seen in this light. In a sentence, the 'child's tie to his mother' develops from his initial 'component instinctual responses' (Bowlby, 1958). The child's attachment to his mother may well be greatly strengthened by the rewards she provides, but in Bowlby's view, the child's attachment does not arise entirely from his learning to associate the mother-figure with the alleviation of his primary needs.

Releasing stimuli, or early percepts, trigger off in the child certain responses. Later in life these percepts may be capable of 'switching on' particular affective behaviour patterns. It may perhaps be said that through imprinting some percepts can acquire a relatively permanent releaser value (Mace, 1962). This is an interesting way of looking at some aspects of the growth of one's likes and dislikes, attitudes, sentiments, predilections or idiosyncrasies.

This is not, of course, an entirely new way of thinking. It is one that will not be strange to those familiar with Gardner Murphy's approach to the problem of personality development (Murphy, 1947). Murphy makes use of the concept of canalisation to account for some aspects of the growth of personality. He maintains that in each human being an initial general innate tendency to respond to stimuli of certain classes becomes in time less general; with time, responsiveness becomes canalised to a narrower range of stimuli, in fact, to the familiar stimuli. There is a tendency for things familiar 'to become better and better liked'. In so far as it makes sense to say that there is a need to perceive (cf. Nissen, 1954), with time this develops into a need to perceive the familiar. Canalisation in Murphy's view is a form of learning to be contrasted with conditioning. As examples of canalisation Murphy (1947) cites some peculiar preferences and attachments observed in doves and pigeons by Craig (1914) and Whitman (1919).

These are the very observations which have been quoted as cases of imprinting.

In a later book (*Human Potentialities, Ch.* 5) Murphy (1960) also considers 'concepts which resemble the concept of canalisation': Freud's cathexis, McDougall's sentiment and Allport's functional autonomy. Above all, according to Murphy (1960), canalisation is much like imprinting as postulated by the early 'naturalist experimenters'. However, the overlapping of concepts raises complex issues which are outside the scope of the present book.

In the development of imprinting, and of affectional responses, the first phase is adience or approach. We shall distinguish in the next chapter between approach-and-stay responses, seen in imprinting, and approach-and-leave responses, seen in exploratory behaviour. We shall be mainly concerned in Chapter 3 with approach-and-stay responses. These are the early filial responses to particular stimulus configurations. For brevity, stimulus configurations may be called figures. The next chapter is devoted to the examination of the character of the figures that evoke approach-and-stay and following responses.

Now we have repeatedly indicated that just staying with a given figure may result in an attachment to that figure. How is such attachment ascertained? The existence of the attachment may be established essentially in two ways: by the test of recognition, and the test of discrimination. These criteria of imprinting will be considered in some detail in Chapter 4. It will be convenient, however, at this stage to indicate what they are, and to relate them to tests of attachment used by Harlow and others in their studies of the development of affectional behaviour patterns in monkeys.

Consider first the recognition test of imprinting. In order to find out whether any procedure leads to imprinting, a number of subjects – say, chicks or ducklings – are 'trained' individually with some figure. On a later occasion the experienced subjects' responses to the figure are compared with the responses of control subjects that have not been given any training. If the experimental animals approach and follow the figure significantly better than the control animals, then the original training procedure must have imprinted them to the figure. Thus, control subjects are clearly needed to establish whether the approach and following of the experimental subjects being tested may or may not be ascribed to imprinting.

In a number of the relatively early studies of imprinting birds were observed responding on more than one occasion to some given object;

cf. Jaynes (1957, 1958a), Moltz and Resenblum (1958a), Salzen and Sluckin (1959a, b). For example, in the last of the studies just cited chicks that had experienced a moving box at one day of age were found to respond more often on later days than control chicks that had not seen the box move before. Although the chicks' exposure to the moving box had been of a few minutes' duration only, it did lead to a degree of imprinting (see fuller discussion of this and similar experiments in Chapter 4).

Recognition tests, or tests of 'affectional retention', have also been used by Harlow in investigating the attachment of his monkeys to the cylindrical object, the cloth mother. The monkeys' attachments were reported by Harlow (1958) to be 'highly resistant to forgetting'. At about eight months of age monkeys that had had experience of the cloth mother appeared to recognise her when tested, and showed strong affectional responses to her; but those monkeys that had had no earlier experience of the cloth mother showed at first only fear or indifference and no signs of affection for her.

Harlow (1958) and Harlow and Zimmermann (1958, 1959) described their 'open-field' test used to investigate the strength of attachment of infant monkeys to their surrogate mothers. The procedure was simply to place a monkey and its cloth mother in a small strange room 'containing multiple stimuli known to elicit curiosity-manipulatory responses in baby monkeys'. In these circumstances any infant monkey that had been raised with a cloth mother would rush to her, clutch her and rub its body against her. The infant would continue clinging to the 'mother' for some time before venturing upon any exploratory activity. It may be asked whether monkeys reared without a cloth mother would not have acted likewise. This is probably not so, because – to quote Harlow and Zimmermann – 'recent evidence indicates that the cloth mother with the highly ornamental face is an effective fear stimulus for monkeys that have not been raised with her'.

Consider now the discrimination test of attachment. This criterion of imprinting has been widely used in some form, both in the earlier and in the more recent studies of imprinting in young precocial birds, e.g. Fabricius (1951a, b), Ramsay and Hess (1954), Jaynes (1956, 1958b), Hess (1957), Guiton (1959), Sluckin and Salzen (1961), Sluckin and Taylor (1964) and Taylor and Sluckin (1964a). To demonstrate imprinting, some subjects are individually 'trained' with one figure, while others are 'trained' with another figure. Then, all the subjects are tested individually in a situation where they may choose between the two figures. Imprinting will have occurred if the animals show a significant preference for whichever is the familiar figure. It may be noted that if all the subjects were trained with one figure only, then, a later choice test would not, strictly, be a test of imprinting. For if this figure were then favoured on test, the experimenter would still not know whether the preference was due to imprinting or to some inherent attractiveness of the figure.

An example of one form of the discrimination test is found in the early work of Ramsay and Hess (1954). These investigators initially exposed newly hatched mallard ducklings to a realistic model of a male mallard; later, this model and a model of a female mallard were used for testing purposes. It was assumed with some justification that without any previous experience ducklings would either choose a female, or, more likely, would not show any preference between a duck and a drake. It was thought inconceivable that the majority of naïve ducklings would prefer the model of a male to the model of a female. Imprinting was considered to have occurred whenever on test the 'trained' ducklings tended to follow, as they often did, the male rather than the female model. It may be noted parenthetically that in this case the test demonstrated attachment which could have been brought about by imprinting and/or by other means. For, since the male model was heated, the ducklings might also have learned to associate the physical comfort of warmth with the model. It is, however, perhaps unlikely that this reward played a dominant rôle in the ducklings' learning.

Discrimination in favour of figure A and against figure B consists simply of movement towards A accompanied, as it often is, by contentment calls, and movement away from B accompanied perhaps by some distress calls. Movement away from an object, particularly if associated with typical noises and other characteristic behaviour, is generally described as fear of the object. Thus, sharp discrimination between two figures, involving movement towards one and away from the other, may often entail some fear responses.

Now the so-called 'open-field fear test', the 'modified open-field test', and the 'home-cage fear test', used by Harlow in his studies of monkey behaviour, appear to be very much like the discrimination test of imprinting. Harlow and Zimmermann (1959), for example, described a procedure whereby infant monkeys which had been raised with a cloth mother were placed individually in a room together with the 'mother' as well as a toy-animal, or 'monster'. The infants showed fear of the monster and ran and clung to the cloth mother. But, as the investigators pointed out, a new and different cloth mother would have been an effective fear stimulus. Thus, the test was in effect one of discrimination between two figures, one familiar and the other unfamiliar (see also descriptions of choice tests in Harlow 1960, 1962). It is noteworthy that the monkeys' exploration of strange objects is normally preceded by some fear of these objects.

Some authors have supposed that imprinting occurs in human babies. As we shall see in Chapters 9 and 10, it may well be that some imprinting-like learning does occur in young children. But the conditions of training and testing in human studies have not been such as to make it possible for imprinting to be demonstrated. Consider, for example, the investigation by Salk (1962) from which it was concluded that auditory imprinting occurs in the baby *in utero* to its mother's heart-beat. Salk's actual finding was that new-born infants, while exposed for four days to heart-beat-like noise, cried less and gained more weight than control infants without this experience. Older children were found to be more easily lulled to sleep by the sound of seventy-two paired beats per minute than by any other sound. These were notable findings. But they did not establish a recognition of heart-beat, nor a preference for this sound resulting from an earlier experience of it. Quite clearly, the effects found could have been due to factors other than imprinting, and cannot by themselves be taken as conclusive evidence of imprinting in human infants.

However this may be, we must now return to imprinting in the narrow, conventional sense of the term. Laboratory studies of imprinting have used precocial birds as subjects, and relatively simple experimental procedures. In our survey of these studies we must consider first of all the conditions in which the initial approach and following responses take place.

Chapter 3

# APPROACH AND FOLLOWING
# RESPONSES

Initial filial responses make their appearance very early in the life of animals, often before any significant learning could have taken place. Although undoubtedly invaluable for the preservation of the species, these responses are not directly related to the survival of the body, that is, to the physiological requirements of food, water, or oxygen, or even the avoidance of noxious stimuli. Nevertheless the approach and following tendency, or drive, is innate and primary. It is perhaps in the same class as the tendencies to explore and manipulate the environment, which are now considered by many students of animal behaviour to be primary rather than acquired or derived from homeostatic, physiological drives (see, for example, Harlow, 1953a,b; Butler, 1953, 1954; Miles, 1958; see also Section IV in Chapter 7).

Approach and following are responses to stimulation; to specify the character of this stimulation has been the aim of much research. Earlier studies by ethologists (cf. Tinbergen, 1951) have demonstrated how various 'sign stimuli' release different kinds of instinctive activity. For example, the courting of a male stickleback is triggered off by the sight of the swollen abdomen and the characteristic posturing movement of the female; the gaping of baby thrushes is released by objects of a certain shape passing horizontally above the nestlings' eyes; and so forth. These sign stimuli are relatively specific, although sometimes a fairly wide range of stimuli can release a given pattern of unlearned responses. What, then, are the features of the stimuli that release approach and following behaviour?

## (i) Models of parents

Early observations had indicated that approach and following could be elicited in newly hatched nidifugous birds by moving animals,

3

persons, and even inanimate objects. Goslings, for instance, in the absence of mother-goose had been found to follow people. Ducklings hatched out from under the hen will, as is well known, follow the hen quite readily. Incubator-hatched ducklings will follow anybody who encourages them to do so by tapping the ground and/or calling while moving away from them. To be effective, this movement away from the young animals should be slow at first but could be speeded up later; in this way the writer and his colleagues have never had any difficulty in evoking following in domestic ducklings.

Fabricius (1951a), Nice (1953), Fabricius and Boyd (1954) and Weidmann (1958) found that wild ducklings of various species could be induced to follow a person walking upright. Hinde, Thorpe and Vince (1956) found that a walking man was a very effective stimulus in starting following in young moorhens and coots; but they also used a model moorhen and other objects for this purpose. Gray and Howard (1957) gave the opportunity to newly hatched domestic chicks to follow individually one or the other of the experimenters; every one of the twelve experimental chicks started to follow in under five minutes. However, human beings and live animals are only occasionally used as objects of approach and following in systematic laboratory research.

Dummy animals and simple models of animals have been used in many experiments. As mentioned earlier, Ramsay and Hess introduced the use of mallard duck models. Subsequently Hess in a series of studies employed a mallard duck decoy suspended from a raised rotating arm pivoted at the centre of a circular runway about five feet in diameter. The dummy was fitted internally with a heating element and a loud-speaker emitting a noise somewhat like the quacking of a duck. Mallard ducklings were placed in the runway a few hours after hatching and were usually kept there with the dummy less than an hour, when they generally followed the dummy for much of the time (see, for example, Hess, 1957, 1958, 1959a,c; Hess, Polt and Godwin, 1959). Hess and Schaefer (1959) used a similar model of a mallard drake as a releaser of following in Leghorn chicks. As indicated earlier, it is not clear to what extent the warmth of the decoy duck helped in these experiments to attract the ducklings and chicks. Most other experimenters have preferred not to associate heat with movement and/or sound employed for evoking following in young precocial birds.

## (ii) Moving objects

Most experiments have been conducted with models not resembling closely any real animals. Fabricius (1951a,b, 1955) and Fabricius and Boyd (1954), while using human beings, live ducks and ducklings, stuffed animals, and models of ducks to elicit following, also used a variety of coloured objects such as boxes, balloons, model railway trucks and so on down to the size of a matchbox. The ducklings of the various species used in the experiments followed these objects in an open field as well as in a runway as short as eight feet in length. It was concluded that the size, shape and colour of the releasing object made, within wide limits, little difference to the intensity of following.

As mentioned above, Hinde, Thorpe and Vince (1956) presented to moorhen chicks a model of a moorhen; this was made of wood and was painted black with black and white stripes on the under-side of the tail; these investigators used also such other objects, as black-and-white boxes, large and small, khaki or green bird-watchers' hides, a red cane basket, and an inflated orange football bladder. Most of these objects could be suspended from a wire which ran the length of the twenty-four yard pen. Any of these objects elicited following, when moved, in some of the moorhen and coot chicks. It was clear that a wide variety of objects could elicit following, and that such following could be brought about entirely without any normal activity of parent birds directed towards their young, such as brooding or feeding.

Ramsay (1951) used a football and a moving box for similar purposes. Hess (1959a) reported that objects resembling the parent bird were found to be no better at releasing following than very simple objects. Hess further claimed that a plain ball was more efficient in eliciting following in chicks than a ball with 'wing and tail-like superstructures', or a ball with wings, a tail and a head; a stuffed cock was found to be a relatively ineffective releaser. Hinde (1961), on the other hand, stated that objects resembling the natural mother were for some species the most effective stimuli both for initial following and imprinting.

Jaynes (1956, 1957, 1958a,b) used small cubes and cylinders for eliciting following in domestic chicks. Salzen and Sluckin (1959a, b) used a red cardboard box, 8 inches × 6 inches × 6 inches high, suspended two to four inches above the floor of the runway by two wires from an overhead cord; the cord could be moved along by means of a hand-wheel. The runway used by Salzen and Sluckin was ten feet long, and the box within it was moved in a jerky manner away from the chick. The trials lasted only a few minutes, and many, but not all, of the experimental chicks followed the box during the trials. Later these experimenters used other types of box as well as dusters suspended in the same way; all the objects appeared to be about equally effective in eliciting following.

Jerky, swinging movement was found by Salzen and Sluckin to be more effective in initiating approach and following in chicks than continuous, constant-speed movement. Earlier, Fabricius (1951a) found that movement of some parts of the body in relation to other parts, as when a duck waddled or a man walked, was an important factor in evoking following in ducklings. Weidmann (1958) likewise noted that a seated person, when swaying from side to side, could elicit approach from ducklings.

### (iii) Intermittent visual stimulation

Observations of the kind mentioned in the last paragraph indicated that a moving object need not necessarily, or at all, move away from the bird to elicit approach from it. Any movement could have been expected to produce this effect, even movement at right angles to the bird's line of vision. Smith (1960) reported this to be so. He used a white disc with a forty-five degree black sector, and he placed it at one end of a ten-foot runway. When the disc was slowly rotated so that the black sector moved round and round, chicks were found to approach it from the other end of the runway; and in the process they ceased to cheep and instead began to make twittering contentment calls. Later, Smith and Hoyes (1961) reported that chicks approached also other patterns moving at right-angles to their line of vision, e.g., slowly-moving horizontal lines, or vertical lines, appearing in a little window level with, and some distance away from, the experimental animals.

The effect of moving a black-and-white pattern across the field of vision at certain speeds is visual flicker. Flicker, however, can be produced more readily by stroboscopic methods, i.e. obscuring a light regularly by means of a shutter, or simply by switching a light on and off, or dimming it, at appropriate intervals. The responses of newly hatched chicks to intermittent sources of light were investigated by James (1959, 1960a,b) and by Smith (1960).

James (1959) initially established that domestic chicks, about two days old, approached intermittent light showing through four small holes at the end of the runway. These unconditioned responses of chicks were later used by James for conditioning purposes; but this will be discussed in later chapters. Smith (1960) independently found that young domestic chicks approached a flickering patch of light, six inches in diameter, appearing just above the floor level at right angles to the floor. This source of intermittent light was found to be, on the whole, as good at releasing initial approaches as the rotating black-sector disc. Later, Smith and Hoyes (1961) established that a variety of sources of flicker could effectively elicit approach responses. But intermittent lights of very small diameters, or of very low intensity, or those placed high above the floor, were relatively ineffective in evoking approach from chicks. Smith and Bird (1963) found that in trials spread over their second, third and fourth days of life chicks showed a greater decrement in approach responses to the flickering patch of light than to the rotating white disc embodying a black sector.

It may be wondered whether the ready responsiveness to movement and flicker is peculiarly characteristic of birds. James (1959) and, later, Moltz (1960) drew attention to earlier investigations of the functioning of the avian eye. An anatomical feature of the bird's eye, but not of that of the mammal, is the pecten. This is an approximately conical structure projecting from the blind spot on the retina towards the pupil. According to Pumphrey (1948) the pecten's main function is probably to supply nutritive substances to the vitreous humour in the space between the lens and the retina. However, it had been said by earlier workers that, by casting shadows onto the retina, the pecten helped the bird to detect movement. While accepting the likelihood that the pecten caused variations in retinal illumination, Pumphrey expressed some doubt as to whether the pecten could enhance the perception of movement. Later, however, Pumphrey (1961) was inclined to regard this theory of the pecten's optical function as sound. More recently Guhl (1962) indicated that the function of the pecten in the avian eye was not entirely clear.

Be this as it may, James (1959) thought that 'a flickering light should be as attractive to newly hatched chicks as a moving object is since the retinal effect of both will be the same'. He found that this was the case, and he held that the approach responses he observed were unconditioned, instinctive responses to fluctuations in lighting. It might have been concluded as a result of these findings that visual flicker was the stimulus essential for imprinting. However, several studies since 1960, including one by James (see Chapter 5), have produced evidence for some imprinting to stationary objects. Therefore, James (1960c) felt obliged to conclude that 'neither real nor artificial movement is necessary for imprinting'.

Turning-to responses may be elicited in newly hatched birds of many species by a variety of unconditioned, low-intensity stimuli (cf. Schneirla, 1956). Schneirla (1959) goes so far as to say that 'low intensities of stimulation tend to evoke approach reactions, high intensities withdrawal reactions with reference to the source'. Moltz (1961) expressed the view that any non-noxious stimulus 'which dominates the sensory environment of the bird during an early period of development should subsequently evoke close following'. But it is clear that visual flicker, in so far as it is the basis of seen movement, tends to be salient in the visual world. It constitutes a far more powerful attraction to the young chick, duckling or gosling than any static feature of the environment. Thus, although retinal flicker is not an irreducible condition of approach responses, it is undoubtedly one of outstanding importance.

### (iv) Intermittent auditory stimulation

Just as intermittent visual stimulation elicits approach responses in newly hatched precocial birds, so does intermittent auditory stimulation. In the early experiments on imprinting, there was a tendency to make the releasers of approach and following resemble the parent bird. Because the parents generally make some noise, the releasers were sometimes also provided with a source of sound. It was clear to the early investigators that a noisy moving object tended to be a better releaser than a silent one. Sometimes intermittent noises alone were used as stimuli, and Lorenz (1935) himself found, and Fabricius (1951a,b) amply confirmed, that acoustic stimuli could effectively release approach and following in ducklings. Collias and Collias (1956) also reported that ducklings were attracted to sources of intermittent noise.

Fabricius established that, to be effective, acoustic stimuli should be simple rhythmical noises; and monosyllabic words, uttered repeatedly, could serve the purpose. Such stimuli were, on the whole, quicker than visual stimuli in eliciting approach from ducklings. Ducklings that failed to follow moving models sometimes did so when appropriate sounds were made, and then followed movement even when the noise ceased. Fabricius thought that the responsiveness to sound of the different species of duck might be related to the habitat of the species.

Collias (1952) found that domestic chicks switched from distress cheeps to contentment chirps in response to short repetitive tones. The chicks preferred sound plus movement to movement alone. Later, Gottlieb (1963c) found that domestic ducklings also responded better to visual and auditory stimulation than to visual stimulation only. Collias reported that some of his chicks ran to the finger that tapped the table, and would run back and forth in response to such stimulation. Collias (1952, 1962) noted a diminution in the responsiveness of chicks to hen's clucking emitted by a loudspeaker after the first post-hatch day.

Collias and Joos (1953) set out to specify by means of spectrographic analysis the common elements in sounds that attracted chicks. They found that these sounds were characterised by '(1) repetitiveness or segmentation, (2) brief duration of the component notes, and (3) the presence of relatively low frequencies'. The clucking and purring of a broody hen have all these attributes, but so have, to some extent, such artificial noises as pencil tapping. Salzen and Sluckin found tapping and knocking to be effective stimuli for eliciting approach in chicks; they also found that, while not all their chicks responded to such noises, those that did respond were able to localise remarkably accurately the source of the noise behind a screen.

In the experiment that Sluckin and Salzen (1961) reported, as many as 450 chicks were tested individually immediately after some limited experience with a small box in a runway. It was found that responsiveness to the acoustic stimulus tended to be related to the chicks' previous experience of box movement; the proportion of chicks responding to sound was significantly greater among those that had experienced fifty jerky movements of the box than among those that had experienced only ten such movements; and the proportion that responded to sound among chicks that had experienced ten jerks of the box was significantly greater than among those that had been near a stationary box. Furthermore, chicks that had actually followed the box were significantly more responsive to sound than those that had failed to follow a moving box.

These results suggested that individual differences in responsiveness to visual and auditory stimuli might be inter-dependent; in other words, that there might be good and poor followers, irrespective of the modality of stimulation. The results indicated that experience of the moving box tended to facilitate approach to sound. A somewhat similar facilitation effect, with visual stimuli only, was personally reported by Smith whose finding was that a patch of light of small diameter evoked more approach responses from chicks that had previously seen a large circle of flashing light than from chicks that had not had such an experience.

A study of Peking ducks, a highly domesticated breed, by Klopfer and Gottlieb (1962a) also shed some light on the relationship between the responsiveness of the young to auditory and to visual stimuli. These investigators used as a stimulus object a mallard duck decoy with a loud-speaker on its underside. The decoy was moved round and round a ten-foot circular course, and each duckling was exposed to it for twenty minutes, ten to twenty hours after hatching. While the model moved, a pre-recorded human voice—'*come*, come, come . . . *come*, come, come' – came out of the loud-speaker. An indication of the relationship between the susceptibility of ducklings to auditory and visual stimuli was obtained by testing each duckling some hours later. The test consisted of two phases: a duckling was exposed for ten minutes to the decoy moving silently, and it was also exposed for five minutes to the sound emanating from the side of the runway while the decoy was absent; the stimuli were presented in one sequence for one bird, in reverse sequence for the next bird, and so on. Now, some ducklings followed the decoy and approached the source of sound, and some responded only to the decoy, or only to sound. The investigators had expected that some ducklings would be more susceptible to auditory stimuli and others to visual stimuli and that these susceptibilities would be independent of each other, and the findings tended to support their expectations (see also Klopfer and Gottlieb, 1962b).

As we have noted earlier, Fabricius thought that the nature of responsiveness to sound could be related to the habitat of the species. Klopfer (1959a) drew attention to behavioural differences between the surface-nesting mallards and the hole-nesting wood-ducks. Mallard ducklings and the young of other surface-nesting species of duck generally see the mother move away from the nest soon after they hatch; such ducklings need to be highly responsive to visual stimuli if they are to follow the mother. On the other hand, the young of species nesting in holes, such as the wood-duck which nests in trees above ground or water, need to respond to auditory stimuli if they are to follow the mother-duck.

Gottlieb (1963b) reported in detail upon the behaviour of the wood-duck in North Carolina. The young hatch out inside holes in trees, and soon thereafter the mother moves out of the hole. About a day after hatching the ducklings also leave the hole and jump onto the ground or water below. The mother begins to make her characteristic calls shortly before leaving the nest and continues making them when outside the nest. The initial low-intensity calls get more frequent and louder until the young emerge from the hole. Gottlieb believes that the prolonged exposure to the duck's calls before the exodus of the young 'allows the ducklings to become aurally imprinted'.

Klopfer (1959b) reported that the young of surface-nesting species of duck, provided they were reared in relative auditory isolation, 'tended to approach most rhythmic, repetitive signals without discrimination'. Similarly, in wood-ducklings Klopfer (1959a) found no initial preferences for any particular auditory signals employed by the experimenter, e.g., tape-recorded calls of various ducks and geese, and repeated human calls, such as 'pip-pip' and 'hello'. But despite their initial catholicity, wood-ducklings were found by Klopfer to become readily attached to particular sounds, more so than ducklings of surface-nesting species.

However, more appears to be known about the responsiveness of young precocial birds to auditory stimulation than about their actual imprinting to such stimulation. In nature, auditory stimulation is usually a component of a configuration of stimuli to which imprinting takes place. It may be that in some species the function of the sounds made by parents is primarily to direct the attention of the young (cf. Gottlieb and Klopfer, 1962; Gottlieb 1963a). In other species, however, auditory imprinting may be as important as visual imprinting, if not more so. There is much scope for further research in this field.

#### (v) Individual differences

There is little doubt that within any one species individuals differ very greatly among themselves in approach-and-stay responsiveness to any particular stimulus configuration. Fabricius and Boyd (1954), for example, remarked – 'One of the most interesting and obscure features of the experiments was the great variation in response to models shown by ducklings with similar "histories". Of any brood successively shown one model at the same age (measured in hours from hatching) some would follow unhesitatingly, others reluctantly, and others not at all'.

Jaynes (1956) noted striking individual differences in the responsiveness of his chicks. Collias and Collias (1956) mentioned variability in the following behaviour among the individuals of the wild waterfowl species which they studied. Gottlieb (1961a) found greater consistency in the following behaviour of ducklings when they were all of the same developmental age, calculated from the onset of incubation, than when they were all of the same post-hatch age. Even so, Gottlieb (1961b) reported considerable individual differences in the responsiveness of mallard and domestic Peking ducklings.

Owing to the great variability in the behaviour of domestic Rhode Island Red chicks, Salzen and Sluckin (1959b) used large numbers of birds in order to establish the percentage incidence of the following response to differing amounts of initial stimulation. They found that 'the incidence of following in a given group of domestic chicks was proportional to the amount of experience of the moving object, and that individuals varied in their readiness to respond as a result of factors other than the amount of experience of the box'.

It is clear that individual differences in responsiveness are most pronounced with stimuli that are only marginally effective. There is little doubt that, given suitable visual and auditory stimulation and plenty of time to respond, most, if not all, newly hatched chicks, ducklings or goslings will show approach and following responses sooner or later. In some studies the relatively slight individual differences in the treatment of the animals during the last stages of incubation, during hatching, and between hatching and the first test, could have been responsible in some measure for the individual differences in responsiveness that were observed.

Whatever the reason, some young birds appear to be more responsive than others to stimuli within a given modality; and also some appear to be more responsive than others to stimuli in one modality than to stimuli in another modality. Better responsiveness to movement by some individuals, and to intermittent sound by others, may, in nature, be all to the good. It may be that individual differences of this kind – a behavioural polymorphism, or polyethism (Klopfer and Gottlieb, 1962b) – can be of advantage to the group as a whole. In this way any type of stimulation would meet with responses from *some* members of the group, which could help the species to survive.

## (vi) Initial attractiveness of stimulus objects

There is no doubt that some forms of stimulation are more effective than others in eliciting early filial responses. Many observations to this effect have been reported, and more recently Smith (1960), Smith and Hoyes (1961) and Smith and Bird (1963) investigated systematically the effectiveness of different stimulus configurations – moving black-and-white patterns, flickering patches of light of varying size and brightness, and so forth – in evoking approach-and-stay behaviour in chicks. Whenever any objects are approached and followed, they are also spasmodically pecked, so that it could be thought that pecking preferences of newly hatched chicks might be indicative of the attractive power of different shapes, colours, etc.

The innate pecking preferences of newly hatched chicks for colours were investigated by Hess and Gogel (1954). Each chick was presented simultaneously with two lots of differently coloured but otherwise identical mash, and its pecks were counted. It was found that domestic chicks have a preference, entirely unlearned, for 'light desaturated colours and that these preferences cannot be explained completely by the lightness of the stimuli'. Later, Hess (1956) reported on the results of a study of natural preferences of chicks and ducklings for small objects of different colour, in which pecks were recorded by electrical counters. Two hundred chicks and one hundred ducklings were tested; all of them had had very limited visual experience prior to the test during which many stimuli were presented all at the same time. Hess found a bimodal distribution of colour preferences in chicks: one peak of the distribution was in the orange region of the colour spectrum, and the other peak in the blue region. The distribution of the preferences in ducklings was a unimodal one, narrower in range than the distribution of the chicks' preferences; the peak of the ducklings' distribution of choices was within the green and yellow-green region of the colour spectrum.

Initial preferences for form have been studied in a manner similar to that used for the determination of colour preferences. Fantz (1957) recorded the numbers of pecks that domestic chicks aimed at several stimulus objects. Using about 350 chicks and 40 stimulus objects, Fantz found that newly hatched chicks of two breeds pecked more at round objects than at angular ones. Since this was so in the case of chicks that had been in the dark prior to the test, there is little doubt that these preferences are innate. Rewarding chicks for pecking at objects of a particular kind did, however, as expected, alter their initial preferences.

Are pecking preferences related, in fact, to the preferences for various stimulus configurations in approach and following? Attempts to throw light on this question in relation to colour were made by Hess and co-workers. Schaefer and Hess (1959) used a number of moving coloured spheres, seven inches in diameter, as objects for eliciting following in domestic chicks. Each chick had a session lasting seventeen minutes, during which a sphere moved forty feet. The different colours used were found to be of unequal effectiveness in eliciting following. In order of effectiveness, from best to worst, the colours were found to be as follows: blue, red, green, orange, grey, black, yellow, white. Chicks were also exposed, one at a time, to one particular coloured sphere on the first day, and were tested on the next day by being allowed to approach any one of five spheres of different colours one of which was the original sphere. On the basis of these tests Schaefer and Hess concluded that the best colours for imprinting were the same colours as the best colours for eliciting initial approach and following (see also Hess, 1959a, and Hess, 1959c). The open question was whether the colour preferences of naïve chicks would have been the same at the age of two days, or three days, as on the first day after hatching.

Gray (1961b) set out to answer this question. He found that, while differential reactions to colour may result from imprinting, they are also a function of maturation. He did not put his chicks in a choice-of-colours situation; his apparatus consisted of three compartments separated by glass; the chick was placed in the middle compartment, and, while one end-compartment was empty, the other contained a revolving coloured circle; the time spent in the vicinity of each colour was automatically recorded. Using inexperienced one-day, two-day, three-day, four-day and five-day old chicks, Gray was able to obtain curves of responsiveness to different colours. The chicks' responsiveness to red was especially good rising to a maximum on the second day, and then gradually tapering off. Gray drew attention to the topographical similarity between his curve of responsiveness and that obtained earlier with a red moving box by Salzen and Sluckin (1959b). Gray found green to be one of the least effective colours, while a yellow live chick was found to be a good releaser of approach to start with, but was no better than the coloured circles on the fifth day.

Hess (1959c) presented data regarding both the chicks' pecking preferences for colours and their preferences for coloured objects in approach and following. He reported that the relationship between these two sets of preferences was an inverse one: while yellow attracted most pecking, and red and blue least, yellow moving objects were least readily followed and red objects and blue objects elicited following most readily.

Schaller and Emlen (1962) used in one of their experiments domestic fowl chicks and Chinese ring-necked pheasants. In this experiment 'naïve' birds were tested by being confronted with a 5-inch × 9-inch cardboard rectangle, attached at right-angles to the end of a rod held by the experimenter. The young birds' preferences in both pecking and approach were tested by presenting them with rectangles of different colours. Many experimental subjects were found to follow the moving test-object after initial retreat; and many individuals pecked at the test object. Black, white, blue, red and green colours were used. Schaller and Emlen found, however, that differences in colour made very little difference, if any, to the intensity of responding. These findings do not necessarily wholly contradict the previous studies which have been quoted. However, it does look as if colour was not a crucial variable in initiating approach and following responses in newly hatched precocial birds.

### (vii) Filial responses and environmental conditions

If the effects of environmental conditons, such as ambient temperature, illumination, noise level, and so on, were more precisely known, it would be possible, by controlling these conditions, to use relatively few experimental subjects for determining the effectiveness of different stimuli in eliciting early filial responses and in bringing about imprinting. Before considering environmental effects, however, it may be wondered whether responsiveness to stimuli releasing approach and following is at all subject to any predictable spontaneous fluctuations. Gray (1962) set out to investigate this problem.

Gray used chicks that had been hatched and kept prior to the test in isolation. He placed each chick in the middle compartment of three; one of the end-compartments contained an age-mate, and the other a fully grown hen. The times spent by the chick during the trial near the age-mate and near the hen were recorded automatically. A fifteen-minute trial like this was made, using a new chick each time, every three hours, right round the clock. The results showed a daily rhythm in the chicks' preferences for the hen, her attraction being greatest around midnight. Gray tested chicks of various ages, ranging from one day to four days after hatching. While the chicks' responsiveness to the hen declined somewhat day by day, the daily rise in responsiveness at midnight occurred at all the ages tried. Clearly, further investigations are needed into the fluctuations in responsiveness to different stimuli in different species.

Kaufman and Hinde (1961) made a study of the factors influencing distress calling in domestic chicks. One important factor was found to be the temperature of the test pen. Distress calls were emitted at a relatively high rate when the temperature of the pen was low, that is, considerably below the chicks' body temperature. Salzen and Tomlin (1963) found that the following response in chicks was delayed by cold. This was probably due to the effect of the low temperature upon the animals' general motor activity. However, Salzen and Tomlin thought it unlikely that this low temperature 'affected the perceptual processes involved in imprinting of which pleasure calling, orientation, incipient following and following are indicators'.

The effect of noise upon the approach and following responses of chicks was investigated by Pitz and Ross (1961). Chicks were tested individually with a moving box in a circular runway for fifteen minutes a day for five consecutive days. It was found that following was in some cases improved when the chick was within some six inches of the box while a loud clapper was sounded. The investigators considered that the intensity of following was related to the degree of arousal which was defined as the 'total amount of stimulation impinging on the organism'. However, the positive influence of noise on following occurred only after the first day, that is, only after some imprinting had taken place. In Chapter 7 we shall consider in some detail such effects in imprinted animals. The effect of noise on newly hatched 'naïve' birds would appear to be still in doubt.

### (viii) Approach and exploration

As we have seen, approach-and-stay behaviour is releasable by fluctuating stimulation rather than by any specific type of stimulus. It is not entirely clear whether non-fluctuating figures which stand out from their background can also in some circumstances evoke approach-and-stay responses. In so far as this may be the case, the range of stimulation eliciting approach and following could be almost as wide as that eliciting exploratory behaviour. The exploring individual approaches objects and places, moving on from object to object and from place to place. In approach and following behaviour the individual tends to approach an object, to stay with it and to approach the object again and again when it recedes. Thus, while exploratory behaviour is relatively variable, approach-and-stay behaviour is relatively stereotyped.

These modes of behaviour may appear to be in contrast, somewhat like the phases of typical instinctive action in higher animals. For various kinds of instinctive behaviour start with relatively variable, so-called, appetitive behaviour, and culminate in relatively stereotyped, consummatory acts. However, exploratory behaviour, although variable, does not, as such, lead up to anything other than gradual satiation; nor, apparently, is it itself a culmination of anything. Similarly, approach and following behaviour, although relatively stereotyped, is not consummatory and does not apparently bring about any drive reduction; nor is it appetitive for it does not lead to anything other than more behaviour of the same kind.

Behaviour of any kind, being a product of natural selection, may be displayed 'regardless of the presence or absence of the need: it may be evoked by internal processes which are independent of such states as hunger or thirst, and by external stimuli which are neutral as far as survival is concerned' (Barnett, 1958). Like exploration, approach-and-stay behaviour has clear survival value; like exploration, it does not apparently result from any visceral need, or state of organic disequilibrium.

If exploration does not result from any need, then how does it arise? Dember and Earl (1957) suggest that exploration is one of the forms of attention, differing from attention in the usual sense only in 'the degree of locomotor involvement'. If exploration is a form of attention, then, approach and following behaviour might also be said to be a form of attention.

An alternative to such a rather strange conclusion is to extend the concept of need so that it embraces the springs of approach and following and of exploratory activity. The tendency to explore is so strong in some animals that the term 'stimulus hunger' has been used to emphasise its impelling nature. Perhaps the tendency to approach and follow sources of intermittent stimulation could also be said to arise from a special 'hunger' or need. We shall return to the problem of primary needs and drives in connection with the consideration of imprinting as a learning process, in the last section of Chapter 7 and in Chapter 9.

Just as any given stimulation can evoke withdrawal or approach according to circumstances, so can any given stimulation bring about either approach-and-stay behaviour (approach and following responses) or approach-and-leave behaviour (exploration). It should be possible in principle to predict from the knowledge of the state of the organism and the environmental conditions how it will respond to the given stimulation. As a rule, precocial animals show a sequence of responses: very early in life, approach and following, and later when attachments have been established, exploratory activity. The young of other species show, of course, hardly any approach and following, though much exploratory behaviour. But exploratory behaviour, or spontaneous alternation, is not universal in young animals; cf. Hayes and Warren (1963). In precocial species it is kept in abeyance by the dominant early filial responses.

Chapter 4

# THE GROWTH
# OF ATTACHMENTS: I

## (i) Tests of imprinting

Early investigators, influenced by Lorenz, believed that the first filial responses to any figure led rapidly to the formation of a strong attachment to that figure. How quickly could such an attachment be formed? Some investigations were particularly concerned with this problem. It soon became clear that the speed with which attachments built up might depend on a variety of factors, e.g. the type of releasing stimulation, the subject's age at initial exposure to it, the activity of the subject at the time of training, and so on. In connection with the early studies an important issue arose, viz., how to judge that an attachment to a figure had actually developed; for the estimation of the speed of formation and strength of attachments could clearly depend on the criteria used for determining their existence.

What, then, constitutes attachment? As we saw in Chapter 2, attachment can be gauged by means of either (1) tests of recognition, or (2) tests of discrimination. If the first of these approaches is used, the experimental subject is repeatedly presented with the same figure. The extent of the attachment thus formed is indicated by the intensity of the animal's approach and following responses when tested with this figure. Imprinting is, of course, presumed only if the responses on test can be taken to have been acquired and are not merely a result of maturation. The other approach to assessing attachment is to 'train' the subject with one figure and test it for choice between the original figure and a new one. Imprinting is considered to have occurred if the animal approaches and follows the original figure rather than the new one, provided it can be shown that this choice is not due to some inherent, innate preference of the animal for the chosen figure.

4

It is quite possible for a newly hatched bird to form a strong attachment to some figure, as judged by the first criterion, but not altogether so, as judged by the second. That is, a subject could vigorously follow the original object, say, some days after the initial experience, but could discriminate only poorly between it and other objects. This would be the case if the gradient of stimulus generalisation were other than steep.

Stimulus generalisation in imprinting has not been very extensively or systematically investigated. But Hinde, Thorpe and Vince (1956) did use one object for 'training' their coots and moorhens, and another object for testing their animals' following responses. The birds often followed the test model, if less persistently than they followed the training model. The fact that generalisation occurred was taken to mean that imprinting was not irreversible; reversibility was in this study regarded as the tendency of animals trained with one object to follow dissimilar objects later.

Jaynes (1956) also reported on generalisation. He exposed domestic chicks either to a moving green cube or to a moving red cylinder. Later each animal was tested with the object of which it had had no experience. Despite a decrement in performance, the chicks showed a considerable degree of generalisation. Moltz (1960), using a model duck and a green cardboard cube, and following a procedure similar to Jaynes's, found some marked stimulus generalisation in Peking ducklings. Cofoid and Honig (1961) 'trained' domestic chicks with a bluish object and tested them with a range of objects, yellow to green in colour. These investigators, too, found a degree of generalisation in their subjects' responses, although not a complete transfer of training.

As we have seen, a subject that strongly responds in a positive manner to the original object but generalises its responses widely to more or less similar objects would be judged to be well attached by our first criterion of imprinting but to be poorly attached by our second criterion. However, a subject that responds positively though feebly to the original object and yet reacts strongly against new objects, running away from them, or otherwise showing fear, would be said to be relatively slightly imprinted by the first criterion, and strongly imprinted by the second, the discrimination criterion.

It may be argued that unless a subject shows discrimination between the original and the new objects imprinting has not been proved. The term, imprinting, as initially used, certainly implied the formation of the ability to discriminate between, and respond differentially to, patterns of movement, form, colour, sound, etc. It is clear that establishing any attachment entails acquiring *some* ability by the subject to differentiate between the familiar and unfamiliar figures. Therefore, some investigators have insisted that only a test of discrimination could establish imprinting. Other investigators have also regarded the less stringent recognition test as an acceptable criterion of imprinting. We shall first consider some studies that have relied on the recognition criterion, and then some others in which the discrimination criterion has been used.

In 1952 Margaret Nice, impressed by Fabricius's findings published in the previous year, set out to imprint onto herself some newly hatched young of the shoveller, redhead and Godwall species of wild duck. Nice (1953) succeeded in this task by calling the day-old ducklings and moving her hand in their presence. All the ducklings followed her, and continued to respond to her calls up to the age of twelve days. It may be assumed, though it does not appear to have been checked, that ducklings without the experience of following the experimenter from the first day would not have followed her when several days old. It does not appear that the ducklings were at any stage tested for choice between the experimenter and other persons.

Jaynes (1957) exposed over fifty young domestic chicks individually for half an hour to a seven-inch green cube moved irregularly up and down a runway ten feet long. Each of these chicks was tested with the cube ten days after its initial experience. It was found that the subjects that had been 'trained' early enough in life tended to follow the stimulus object. In another study Jaynes (1958a) trained chicks by exposing them to a moving object for varying periods of time during the first four days of life. The chicks were tested individually with the same object at thirty and seventy days of age. Some of them were found to be attached to the object despite the very long interval between the training sessions and the test.

Another study relying on the recognition criterion of imprinting was that of Moltz and Rosenblum (1958a). Using a runway and a moving object quite similar to Jaynes's, Moltz and Rosenblum exposed Peking ducklings individually to the test object twenty-five minutes a day, day after day from the day of hatching, for fifteen consecutive days. Having retained thirteen strong initial followers, the investigators computed for each of these birds a 'moving score' based on the time spent near the moving object. Figure 1 shows median moving scores for the group as a function of trials. Following was found to be most intense between the third and sixth days. Thereafter following gradually diminished in intensity, and this led the investigators to conclude that imprinting was no less irreversible than other types of learned behaviour. It may be noted that in this study reversibility referred to a decrement in responding to the original object rather than to a generalisation of responses to strange objects.

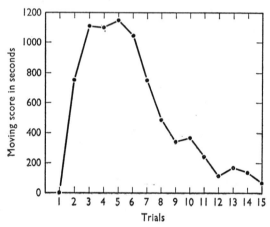

*Fig. 1: Median moving-scores as a function of trials (from Moltz and Rosenblum, 1958a)*

In the same category with regard to the criterion of imprinting as the studies considered above is also the first experiment of the series conducted by H. James. James (1959) used as his subjects thirty-six domestic chicks obtained from a commercial hatchery and housed in the laboratory in individual brooder-compartments. The stimulus used was not a moving object but a flickering light; *vide* Chapter 3. Starting at the age of approximately forty-eight hours, each chick was given a series of trials. Each trial began with the chick facing a side wall in the centre of the ten-foot runway. A trial consisted of exposing the chick for five minutes to intermittent lights showing through holes at one or other of the two ends of the runway. Each chick was given two trials a day for seven days and one trial on the eighth day. As the trials went on, one or other of the ends of the runway would be illuminated, the sequence being such as to ensure that the chick did not develop a habit of always turning one way. The illumination was made intermittent at three different frequencies, and chicks were assigned at random for the duration of the experiment to one of the three flash rates. The distance of each chick from the flashing light was measured every 30 seconds over each five-minute trial. The

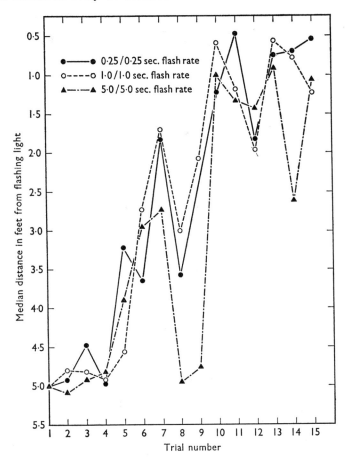

Fig. 2: *Median distance, in feet, of each group of chicks from that end of the runway at which the light was flashing, as a function of trial number (from James, 1959)*

findings are set out in Fig. 2. As the trials went on, each chick spent more and more time beside the flashing lights, pecking at them, or walking slowly in front of them pecking at the sawdust on the floor.

As mentioned earlier, Salzen and Sluckin (1959a, b) 'trained' chicks with a moving box and later tested them with the same box. Because the experimental chicks were not tested for their ability to discriminate between the familiar object and new ones, these investigators were reluctant to describe their chicks as imprinted. The procedure was to expose individually one group of chicks to fifty jerky movements of the box, a second group to ten movements, and a third group to the stationary box for a period of one minute. These experiences were given to chicks on the day after hatching. Different groups of chicks

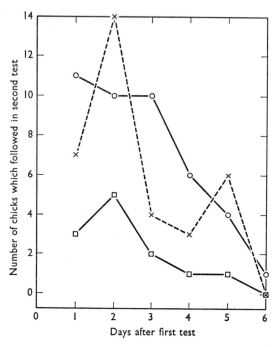

Fig. 3: *Numbers of birds in each group of 25 chicks which made at least one response to 10 movements of the box in tests made from 1 to 6 days after the first experience*

     ○:   *50 experiences in the first test*
     ×:   *10   ·,   ,, ,, ,, ,,*
     □:   *0   ,,   ,, ,, ,, ,,*
(*from Salzen and Sluckin, 1959b*)

were subsequently tested from one to six days after training (in that study this was called 'the first test'). Figure 3 summarises the findings. The experienced chicks showed significantly more positive responses to the box than those that had not seen a moving box before.

A test of discrimination between familiar and unfamiliar figures used in the imprinting situation was devised long ago by Pattie (1936), who himself was not at all explicitly concerned with imprinting. Pattie was, in fact, attempting to discover whether the gregarious tendency in young chicks was innate or acquired. He kept single chicks in visual isolation from other chicks until they were four days of age, and then tested them individually for sociability for thirty minutes a day, day after day for six days. In the test situation the chick was placed in a compartment in which two walls opposite each other were made of glass; through one of these were visible two chicks, and through the other, two white mice. When the experimental chick was near one or the other of the glass walls, its weight depressed the floor in that area, closing an electric circuit, which then registered the total time spent by the subject close to the mice and close to the stimulus chicks. Pattie found that on the whole chicks showed no 'gregarious instinct' in that they did not clearly prefer their own kind to mice.

Thus, Pattie's main experiment had no direct bearing on imprinting; however, his control experiment, remarkable in its simplicity, was a prototype of the imprinting discrimination test. Pattie used forty-two chicks in the control experiment, the same number as in the main study, but while his experimental subjects had been reared in visual isolation from other chicks until four days of age, his control subjects had been reared socially, in small groups. These control chicks were confronted at four days of age, like the others, with the choice between two chicks and two white mice, and again so, day after day for six consecutive days. They were found to spend very much more time by the glass wall near the stimulus chicks than near the mice. Pattie concluded that gregariousness in chicks was a result of very early experience of other chicks. The attachment of communally reared chicks to their own kind may well have resulted from imprinting. The attachment could, of course, have been, in part, due to associative learning; for, at ambient temperatures below optimum, the warmth resulting from contact might have been instrumental in producing mutual attachment of chicks. However, there is evidence (see later section of this chapter) that when reared communally, chicks imprint to one another.

A discrimination test of imprinting was employed by Fabricius (1951a) to find out if the ducklings that he used would approach and follow some familiar object and turn away from an unfamiliar one. Fabricius and Boyd (1954) and Fabricius (1955) reported two experiments, with twelve ducklings in each, in which discriminatory responses to two models were investigated. The subjects in one group of ducklings were shown a balloon at the first trial, and those in the second group were shown a brown box. At subsequent trials, after an interval of two or more days, some ducklings were shown only the original object and some were shown only a new object; others, however, were given a choice between the familiar and strange models. Some ducklings followed a strange object as well as the familiar one, but in all cases responses to the strange objects were less positive and lacked the accompaniment of contentment calls. In the choice trials, the familiar models were preferred to the new ones.

Jaynes (1956) used a discrimination test in one of his experiments. He exposed individually six chicks for half-an-hour a day, over the first four days of life, to a moving green cube, and six other chicks to a moving red cylinder. On the fifth day each chick was presented with a choice of the two objects, now motionless. The findings were clear-cut: all the subjects with previous experience of the cube went to the cube, and all with previous experience of the cylinder went to the cylinder. In a later experiment Jaynes (1958b) used eight chicks, again exposing each separately to a moving object (a red cylinder) for thirty minutes a day during the first four days of life. After each session stimulus generalisation was investigated by exposing each chick for a short time to objects differing in shape and colour from the original object. Then, on the fifth day each chick was tested during a forty-five-minute session for discrimination between the familiar object and one of the strange objects when both these moved in the runway at the same time. Jaynes found that his chicks tended, on the whole, to follow the familiar object rather than any of the unfamiliar ones.

Hess (1957) used the discrimination method of testing ducklings for imprinting, evolved earlier by Ramsay and Hess (1954), and described briefly in Chapter 2. Later studies employing the choice test tended, however, to favour techniques more like those of Pattie or Jaynes. Guiton (1959) trained chicks individually to a moving object in a circular runway, the day after hatching. Each chick was faced at four days of age simultaneously with two objects, one of which was old and one new. The animals tended to respond positively to the familiar object and negatively to the new one; an unfamiliar object would only be accepted and followed when the original object was not available. Sluckin and Taylor (1964) trained chicks two days after hatching to a moving object for three hours, and tested them within the next hour for discrimination between it and another object. In one experiment the old and the new objects moved, on test, in the runway; in another experiment the objects were stationary; in both cases chicks discriminated between the objects in favour of the one which they had already experienced. Smith and Hoyes (1961) in one of their experiments exposed six chicks to the rotating black-and-white disc, referred to in the last chapter, for short periods over seven days, and similarly exposed six other chicks to a disc of flashing light. On the eighth day each chick was confronted with both discs at once, placed some distance apart. In all cases the subjects approached and stayed with the familiar one of the two stimuli.

### (ii) Duration of attachments

Once formed, how long can attachments last? Lorenz (1935, 1937b) thought imprinting to be irreversible. This might imply no generalisation to new figures, or stability of the following response to any given figure, or both (cf. Moltz, 1960). As we have noted earlier, generalisation occurs in imprinting, just as it does in conditioning. We shall now consider the stability of imprinted attachments.

The early observations of following in the different species of wild duck indicated that strong following waned some time around three weeks after hatching (Fabricius, 1951a; Nice, 1953). Fabricius and Boyd (1954) found that mallard ducklings ceased to follow at about ten days of age; but these ducklings, having been housed communally, could have become imprinted more strongly to one another than to any other figure; had each been kept in isolation, the ducklings might have continued to follow longer. In the investigations of Hinde, Thorpe and Vince (1956) the responses of moorhens decreased markedly at four to five weeks, and those of coots at seven to eight weeks.

In some of the earlier studies of imprinting investigators tended to use figures that offered stimulation in more than one modality. Later, when more was learned about the essential features of the releasers of approach and following, simpler stimulus configurations began to be used. In laboratory studies it was convenient to have relatively short imprinting sessions. And in this way the effects of quite limited amounts of initial experience began to be observed. Under such circumstances the duration of attachments was found to be quite short; that is, these attachments were found to be relatively unstable. Salzen and Sluckin (1959b) found that a few minutes' experience of a moving box on the first day after hatching did leave some 'memory trace' of the box in their experimental chicks; for, on test, the experienced chicks followed better than inexperienced control ones for up to five days after training.

What is more, these investigators found two days after training a difference in performance between subjects that had initially experienced the moving box for approximately two minutes and those that had initially experienced the box for approximately eight minutes. Thus, stability of attachment appeared to be a function of the extent of initial experience. Jaynes (1958a), in other circumstances, also found this to be so. His experimental chicks were more strongly imprinted, and were tested thirty and seventy days after training; responsiveness on test was related to the amount of initial experience with the moving object. Jaynes's finding about the durability of imprinting in chicks was amply confirmed by Guiton (1961). Using boxes emitting clucking noises, Guiton found that well imprinted chicks only ceased to follow such moving objects at between eight and twelve weeks of age.

The various researches just mentioned were concerned with relatively long-term retention of training in imprinting. Sluckin and Taylor (1964), on the other hand, investigated the effects of imprinting some minutes rather than some days after initial 'training'. They used both the recognition and the discrimination tests of retention. In one experiment domestic chicks were exposed two days after hatching to a moving object for three hours. Some of these chicks were tested individually for following the object almost immediately after training and some half-an-hour later. Following was found to be significantly better half-an-hour after the training session. This improvement in following after a time interval was considered to have been associated with the recovery from 'drive satiation' which had resulted from the long imprinting session.

In another experiment Sluckin and Taylor trained individually, as before, forty-eight chicks, and then tested each for discrimination between the original and new moving objects in four batches as follows: twelve, almost immediately after training, twelve after five minutes, twelve after fifteen minutes, and twelve after forty-five minutes. Discrimination scores were based on observations of the subjects' preferences, and ranged from —1 to +2 for each chick (thus, the total maximum score per batch of twelve could have been twenty-four). The results are set out in Fig. 4. It will be seen that discrimination continued to improve as the time interval between training and testing lengthened. Again, recovery from 'drive satiation' was thought to be responsible. In yet another experiment similarly trained chicks were tested for discrimination between the initial object and a strange one when these objects were stationary. In these circumstances discrimination tended to be slightly poorer after a time interval than immediately after training. It is a matter for speculation as to why there was no improvement in discrimination after a time interval when conditions of testing differed markedly from those of training.

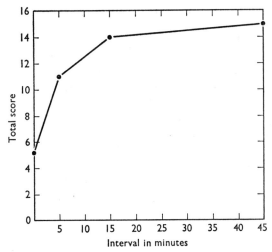

*Fig. 4: Total discrimination scores after different time intervals (from Sluckin and Taylor, 1964)*

### (iii) Imprinting and socialisation

Considering the extreme non-specificity of the stimuli that initially elicit approach and following, it may well be expected that the young become imprinted not only to their mother, but also to one another, and to their own kind in general. This would ensure that like will stay with like, all members of one species recognising one another as such. Learning the characteristics of the species has been called supra-individual learning.

One might wonder, as Pattie (1936) did, whether any animals instinctively recognise other members of their species. Such instinctive recognition might occur in some species but not in others. Lorenz (1935) noted that the young of many birds did not behave as if they could instinctively recognise their own kind; when reared in isolation they did not respond later in a normal manner to members of their own species; and when reared by human beings, they behaved towards people as if people were their natural companions.

Schooland (1942) carried out extensive experiments with ducklings and chicks in the hope of finding out which features of the birds' behaviour were innate and which were learned. In one series of investigations ducklings and chicks were reared in mixed groups for ten and for eighteen days. Such animals were individually tested for choice between a chick and duckling, or between a group of chicks and a group of ducklings. Schooland found a tendency for like to approach like, but in a substantial number of cases tested, ducklings approached chicks and chicks approached ducklings. Thus, the communal rearing was not without some effects.

Some unusual attachments of birds have on occasions been reported. For example, Nice (1950) described a case of a young captive redwing whose companions were a nighthawk, a meadowlark, and people. The redwing developed some marked attachment to the nighthawk, but its bond to people was stronger still and this continued after the bird had become fully independent. Such attachments could, of course, have easily resulted from reward conditioning. But there seemed a strong case for experimental investigations into the rôle of imprinting in such situations.

As mentioned earlier, Cushing and Ramsay (1949) reared mixed families of birds in which the foster-mother and her young were of different species; various hens and ducks were used as foster-mothers for turkey poults, young quail, young pheasant, and different species or breeds of ducklings and chicks. Heterospecific 'families' were readily established. It was clear that the formation of family bonds in a number of bird species did not depend on heritable determinants. It was not quite clear whether intra-family bonds were formed among siblings as well as between the foster-mother and her young. Alley and Boyd (1950) considered that parent-young recognition, which they studied in the coot, was a part of the larger problem of intra-specific, species recognition. Ramsay (1951) thought that recognition of members of the family depended on imprinting. If this is so, it could be asked whether flocking, too, was established through imprinting. Collias (1952) discussed in these terms the growth of 'social attachments' in chicks. In a more recent paper Collias (1962) held that the early stages of socialisation lay in the formation of bonds between the mother and her young, and that this was followed by mutual attachments among the young themselves, and, generally, among members of the species.

Fabricius (1951a) noted a strong flocking tendency in ducklings. This tendency could be overcome in a duckling only by imprinting it initially to something other than another duckling. Weidmann (1958) considered that in newly hatched ducklings the same basic response was involved in the approach and following of the first available moving figure as in flocking. Gray (1958) remarked that what he termed the 'joining response' of infant siblings was set off by the same kind of stimulation as prompted the following of parents; the approach and following hardened with time into lasting attachments. Weidmann (1958) expressed the view that imprinting entailed the development of a drive for social contacts.

Ducklings reluctant to follow a moving model were induced by Ramsay and Hess (1954) to do so by the expedient of putting them in the company of other ducklings, previously imprinted with that model. Klopfer (1959a) used trained 'leader' ducklings to stimulate three to four other ducklings to follow the experimenter when they would not do so otherwise. Such findings indicated the importance of the social element in imprinting behaviour in the laboratory. However, the next step in the understanding of the relationship between imprinting to mother-figure and to siblings was reached largely as a result of Guiton's studies.

Guiton (1958) found that, unlike chicks reared in isolation, chicks reared in groups after reaching the age of about three days did not attempt to follow a moving object, when first confronted with one. He considered that this cessation of responsiveness was due to the fact that by the time the socially reared chicks were some three days old, they were well attached to one another; see Guiton (1959). Later, Sluckin and Salzen (1961) entirely confirmed Guiton's findings. James (1960b), too, reported that socially reared chicks were less apt to approach a flickering light than chicks which had been reared singly. It was clear that in all these cases prior imprinting hindered or prevented subsequent imprinting.

Further experiments by Guiton (1961) showed that chicks imprinted to single objects in groups were imprinted less effectively than single chicks. As in the earlier study of ducklings by Klopfer (1959a), such subjects generally followed one or two leaders rather than the object, the leadership frequently passing from individual to individual.

Guiton suggested that the relative ineffectiveness of group training might be partly due to the fact that, in the course of following, each chick responded for part of the time to other chicks rather than the training figure, in this way becoming imprinted both with the figure and the chicks. For a given period of training, communally trained chicks spent less time following the figure, as such, than individually trained chicks. Since the intensity of attachment to a figure tends to be proportional to the time of exposure to it, it is not surprising that group training in which each chick appears to be exposed for only part of the time to the figure is relatively ineffective.

Whatever the actual social behaviour may involve, it depends on the ability of the individual to recognise members of its own species and the tendency to approach and stay with them. Pattie (1936) showed that social behaviour in chicks developed as a result of being reared with their own kind. Taylor and Sluckin (1964a) went a little further. They reared some newly hatched chicks in pairs; they also reared some singly, but with a cardboard box moving round a circular runway. After a day in these conditions all subjects were tested individually in the middle part of a rectangular runway. The two ends of this runway were fenced off; one of them contained a chick, and the other the rotating cardboard box. The subjects reared socially tried to 'break through' the wire mesh screen separating them from their earlier companion. The subjects reared with the moving box stayed as near the box as they could get and vigorously pushed their heads through the mesh, attempting to reach the box.

Such studies indicate how strong the imprinted social ties can be. What happens, however, when no ties are allowed to form? Baron and Kish (1960) set out to find out how early social isolation could disrupt the usual aggregative behaviour of the domestic chick. These investigators reared some chicks in complete social isolation, some chicks in pairs, and some in a flock during the first four weeks of their life. At the end of that time observations of social reactivity of each chick were conducted. The apparatus consisted of a test compartment, with two adjoining display compartments separated from the former by wire-mesh screens. The chick to be tested was placed for two hours in the test compartment, while another chick, a 'stimulus animal', was in one of the two display compartments. The time spent by the experimental chick during the test in the one-third of the area closest to the stimulus animal was automatically recorded. It was found, to start with, that during the test at four weeks of age the socially reared chicks and those reared in pairs spent significantly more time near the stimulus chick than did the chicks reared in isolation.

In the second stage of the experiment by Baron and Kish all the chicks were put together into a communal living cage. At ten weeks of age, all subjects were tested once again in the same way as at four weeks. This time there were no significant differences in behaviour between the groups of birds initially reared under different conditions. Imprinting of chicks with one another must have been partly responsible for the greater tendency of the socially reared birds to approach at four weeks of age the stimulus animal. Whether imprinting was also, in part, responsible for the later socialisation of the chicks initially reared individually is at present an open question. There are some strong indications that imprinting would be unlikely to occur in chicks as old as four to ten weeks. And yet this possibility cannot be ruled out. We shall consider evidence one way and the other in Chapter 6.

Socialisation that is rooted in relatively early experiences, and which probably depends in some considerable measure on imprinting, has been termed by Scott (1958a), primary socialisation. Hess (1962a) goes so far as to say that 'imprinting refers to the primary formation of social bonds in infant animals'. At any rate, primary socialisation appears to determine the species to which an individual becomes attached; it is usually the individual's own species, but in special circumstances attachments to alien species may be formed. Secondary socialisation – as Scott calls it – to animals and/or to human beings takes place later in life. Presumably, secondary socialisation depends mainly or wholly on instrumental, reward learning.

Scott reports that puppies which are allowed to run wild until the age of about twelve weeks may be subsequently tamed; this would be secondary socialisation to human beings. However, such dogs always remain somewhat timid and less responsive to people than dogs trained earlier in life. In complete contrast, puppies raised by hand from an early age grow up free from fear of human beings. In this case, as in many others, the result of early learning appears to differ from the result of later learning. Early and later learning will be considered in Chapter 8, and the special effects of early experiences will be looked at in Chapter 10.

There is evidence that young birds can become attached to more than one figure at once (cf. Fabricius, 1951a; Hinde, Thorpe and Vince, 1956; Jaynes, 1957; Guiton, 1959). Puppies that have been in contact from an early age with both dogs and people do become strongly attached to both. We may wonder with Scott (1958a) whether 'improved' methods of upbringing of human infants might not perhaps 'increase the variety of people whom they can later tolerate and to whom they can successfully adjust in adult relationships'.

### (iv) Courtship fixations

However well attached an immature animal may be to some particular figure, it ceases to approach and follow that figure as it grows up. This in itself, however, does not necessarily indicate that the animal then 'forgets' its attachment. For it appears that the choice of the objects of courtship by mature individuals may be influenced sometimes by their early imprinting experiences.

As mentioned in Chapter 1, Craig (1908) quoted some pertinent studies of pigeons by his contemporary, Whitman. Whitman found that some passenger pigeons, now an extinct species, which had been reared by ring-doves, later mated with ring-doves rather than with their own kind. Craig concluded that pigeons had no innate tendency to court birds of any particular kind. He thought that they learned to court individuals of the species of their nursing-parents, by associating them with feeding. The possibility of non-rewarded exposure learning influencing the direction of the sexual drive was not then considered.

Craig (1914) further reported a case of four male 'blond' ring-doves which were removed from their parents after the age of weaning, but long before maturity, and reared in visual isolation from other doves. These doves directed their sexual responses at the age of one year towards the hand of the experimenter which to them had been a familiar object. When confronted with a female, they ignored it at the start, although later slowly learned normal copulation. Even after accepting the female dove as an object of courtship, the four males still continued to react positively to human beings.

Whitman, at one time, kept indoors a mourning-dove; later when the mating season came, Whitman found that the dove began to show interest in the experimenter himself (Carr, 1919). Carr, the psychologist editor of Whitman's writings, suggested the following explanation for the dove's strange behaviour:

The bird may have been reared, while with the dealer, in entire isolation from pigeons, and the human environment was perhaps the only one in which it lived with any degree of intimacy; and this early training may have so fixed its habits of interest and attention that they persisted for some time after being given companions of its own kind.

Years later, Goodwin (1948) described 'some abnormal sexual fixations in birds', again mostly pigeons, which he had kept between 1933 and 1940. One turtle-dove courted and attempted to copulate with domestic pigeons. A wood pigeon made sexual displays to domestic pigeons. A domestic pigeon courted stock-doves. A magpie was fixated on domestic pigeons. All these birds had been separated from their own kind to varying degrees, and habitually saw birds of species other than their own in the neighbourhood.

Räber (1948) reported that a male turkey, imprinted to man, directed its courtship only towards men or dummies of men; it fled from, or attempted to fight, human beings carrying handbags or similar dangling objects. However, Räber found that the stimuli which would initiate attempts at copulation did not appear to be the same as those that elicited courtship; the turkey-cock, although never courting turkey-hens, did mate with them.

More recently, Steven (1955) reported a case of a gosling, of the lesser white-fronted goose species, that became attached to human beings and rejected individuals of such species as the black swan; the rôle of reward learning in the formation of this particular tie was not clear. Von Frisch (1957) described the behaviour of a purple heron which had been raised in captivity; this animal addressed its courting, nesting and mating responses towards its foster-parent, the investigator. Hess (1959c) imprinted a jungle fowl cock onto himself, keeping the cock away from its own kind for the first month of its life; the cock subsequently courted human beings rather than females of its own species.

Hediger (1950) mentions a tame emu in the Basle Zoo which regularly, during the winter mating season, tried to mate with its keeper. Smaller animals – reports Hediger – often get attached to the human leg, or shoe, rather than to the whole person. Hediger (1955) quotes an earlier interesting account by Hodge of the method of cross-breeding between two llama species, the alpaca and the vicuña. Apparently this can only occur when a new-born male vicuña has been attached to mother alpaca; only such males will later pair with alpacas.

Among the more bizarre cases reported is one described by Heinroth and Heinroth (1959). At the Schönbrunn Zoo in Vienna a

5

white peacock was reared with giant Galapagos tortoises. Thereafter the bird would not bestow his affections on anything but these tortoises. Lorenz (1955) stated that birds of many species, when imprinted to man, would refuse to copulate with 'conspecifics'; this, according to Lorenz, had been observed, amongst others, in parrots, cockatoos, eagle owls and Andean geese. Nicolai (1956) reported that bullfinches, which had been reared apart from their own kind, would become attached to, and would court, their human keeper.

It is noteworthy that such fixations are not often exclusive. Whitman's mourning-dove was finally mated with a female of its own species. Goodwin (1948) once had a female domestic pigeon that reacted sexually to himself, but this bird was later successfully paired to a male domestic pigeon; this female, however, continued to react to the man even after it acquired a mate of its own species. Bullfinches attached to a human keeper were said by Nicolai (1956) to switch over to 'a conspecific of the opposite sex' if given the opportunity during their first autumn or winter. Kear (1960) reported that a female hawfinch, which treated the experimenter as her mate, also appeared earlier to behave normally with a mate of her own species.

Fabricius (1962) pointed out that sexual imprinting, although known to occur in nidicolous birds (whose newly hatched young stay in the nest and are fed there) such as jackdaws, ravens, owls, bitterns, budgerigars, doves, or finches, is quite rare in nidifugous species. At the Wildfowl Trust at Slimbridge vast numbers of ducks and geese have been reared with hens as foster-parents; and yet, hardly ever have these ducks or geese been observed courting the domestic fowl.

While inappropriate sexual fixations occur in nidicolous species, those are the species in which the presence of imprinting is extremely difficult to establish. For the nidicolous newly hatched young are helpless; they are fed entirely by their parents or foster-parents, and so conditioning is likely to occur from the start. Therefore, while it is often possible in nidifugous species to separate the effects of conditioning and imprinting, in nidicolous species of birds, attachments, including sexual fixations, cannot be readily assigned to one or another type of early training.

Some carefully controlled laboratory investigations of the influence of imprinting on the behaviour of mature nidifugous birds were carried out by Guiton (1961). He imprinted male domestic chicks in the first week of life to cardboard figures, and subsequently studied the development of their agonistic and courtship responses. Two figures were used, differing in shape and colour, but both emitting clucking noises. Some chicks were trained with one model and some with the other; some birds were trained individually, and others were trained in groups of five chicks at a time. Control birds were not trained to follow a model, but were habituated to the experimental situation shortly before their first test at six weeks of age. Guiton tested individually all the imprinted cockerels from the age of seven days until the age of twenty-four weeks. The test was one of discrimination between the familiar and the unfamiliar models. Tests of discrimination were also carried out on the control chicks from the age of six weeks until the age of twenty-four weeks. Some of the birds, when older than twenty-four weeks, were given further tests of the same kind, and also additional simultaneous choice tests between a familiar model and a stuffed hen or cock.

The imprinted birds were found to continue following the moving figures up to the age of eight to twelve weeks, the intensity of following decreasing gradually. The individually trained birds tended to respond more strongly and more selectively to the familiar figures than those trained in groups; see Chapter 6 about effects of individual and communal rearing. At any rate, the imprinted cockerels tended at eight weeks of age, and sometimes earlier, to be aggressive towards the figures in the same way as birds of that age are aggressive towards their companions. The control birds displayed no such responses towards the models. The findings concerning courtship were somewhat equivocal. Two cocks courted the training model, continuing this until the time of the last test at fourteen months. Four others, however, did not respond to the training model, but attacked and courted a stuffed cockerel. The first two birds reacted not only to the training but also to a stuffed hen and cockerel; in choice situations they preferred the stuffed animals to the figure with which they had been trained.

It appears that there are degrees of imprinting; under laboratory conditions, lasting and discriminating attachments to made-up objects are not easily achieved. The durability and specificity of attachments depend, amongst others, on the initial effectiveness of the figure and on the total time of exposure, and exclusiveness of exposure, to the figure. Irreversibility, in the sense of both durability and limited stimulus generalisation, is, no doubt, usual under 'natural' conditions; it is, however, relatively rarely attained otherwise.

Imprinting appears to vary in extent or thoroughness like other forms of learning.

During the initial stages of imprinting the subject approaches and follows a figure, and gradually becomes attached to the figure. This attachment may show itself later in types of performance not shown in the early stages. What is learned is not the performance, but the characteristics of the object of attachment. The same object will elicit different kinds of approach, depending on the internal state of the organism. The early responses of approach and following give way, in some male subjects, to aggressive approaches, and then, to courtship responses. The condition of the organism determines in what way the attachment will show itself. Just as a variety of stimuli can, in the first place, evoke filial responses, so also later a variety of stimuli can evoke sexual responses. However, what gives stimuli their sexual value depends in some measure on the early experiences of the subject; in other words, early experiences of the subject modify the releasing value of the usual sexual stimuli.

This was effectively shown by Schein and Hale (1959) who used as experimental subjects turkey poults injected with androgen. By means of injections male sexual behaviour was induced in otherwise immature turkeys. Some young turkeys were raised in visual isolation from their own kind, and others were raised in groups. A variety of stimuli were used to evoke sexual behaviour. Birds reared in isolation gave sexual responses predominantly to the observer's hands. Birds reared in groups, reacted predominantly to a dummy poult head (a female head is normally a sexual releaser for socially reared adult male turkeys). Thus, early experiences and hence existing attachments, while not influencing the character of sexual behaviour as such, determined the objects at which the behaviour was directed; see also Hale and Schein (1962).

Bambridge (1962) went further; his experimental animals, male chicks injected with male sex hormone, had previously been deliberately imprinted to one of two moving objects, identical in shape, one of which was blue and the other yellow. After ten hours of training a day during the early days, the chicks were confronted on the nineteenth and twentieth day with the blue and the yellow models in the circular runway. The birds almost invariably trod the particular objects with which they had been imprinted.

Guiton (1962) also injected some of his male chicks with the male hormone, testosterone. First, however, he reared them for thirteen weeks in visual isolation from each other, but not from the experimenter. The still immature injected cockerels were tested for choice between a stuffed crouching pullet and a yellow rubber glove. The birds were found to prefer the glove. Other cocks remained uninjected; these were tested at five months of age. Although still showing attachment to the familiar hand, they preferred the stuffed hen.

Earlier reports indicated that domestic hens and cocks which had not been with the other sex before sexual maturity could often mate quite successfully. Fisher and Hale (1957) reported that males reared in isolation waltzed to hens but did not mount them to start with; females reared in isolation tended to crouch to humans rather than to courting cocks. Under conditions of normal poultry management the domestic fowl and turkey direct their sexual responses, according to Fisher and Hale, to both man and members of their own species. Wood-Gush (1958) reared cocks in isolation until the age of six-and-a-half months, at which age their responses to hens were compared with those of cocks reared in the usual way. There was no clear-cut difference in the behaviour of the experimental and the control animals. Kruijt (1962) reported that Burmese red jungle fowl cocks brought together with hens before the age of ten months could still be mated success-fully. However, if kept in isolation longer than that, then successful copulatory behaviour could not be achieved.

The most that can be said is that objects of sexual responses are sometimes selected by mature precocial birds not on the basis of any innate preference but on the basis of their resemblance to objects of early filial responses. Whether this applies in any measure at all to mammals, including human beings, will be considered in Chapter 10. Research tasks posed by any such hypothesis are quite formidable.

# Chapter 5

# THE GROWTH
# OF ATTACHMENTS: II

### (i) Movement of the subject

The object of the following responses is a retreating figure. In keeping up with it, the subject must continue to move. Is the subject's own movement a factor in imprinting? Hess (1957, 1958, 1959a, 1959c, 1962a) has maintained that imprinting is bound up with the effort expended by the animal in moving towards the source of stimulation.

Hess initially exposed mallard ducklings to a model moving round a circular runway; the duration of the exposure was kept constant, but the speed of the model was varied. As a result, the distance travelled by the model and by the ducklings which closely followed it also varied. The ducklings were then tested for their ability to discriminate between the familiar model, now stationary, and a strange, differently coloured model, either moving or stationary. Those ducklings that had initially covered more ground in following now chose more frequently the original model.

Hess further reported that when his ducklings travelled a fixed distance, then the degree of imprinting, judged by recognition and discrimination tests, remained constant even though the time taken to cover the distance varied a great deal. Hess confirmed this for different distances: in one of his experiments the ducklings had to travel only $12\frac{1}{2}$ feet, while in another, as much as 100 feet. In the case of the hundred-foot distance the training period for some subjects was ten minutes, and for others, thirty minutes; and yet such differences in the strength of imprinting as were found between the groups were not statistically significant.

Hess concluded that the intensity of imprinting did not depend on the time of exposure to the moving object, but rather on the distance covered and, therefore, the effort exerted or the energy expended by the bird in the process of following the object. Partly to put this to a further test, Hess (1958) ran some ducklings in a runway in which four-inch hurdles had been placed, and these obstacles forced the animals to exert more effort than did animals which followed an object in an ordinary runway. It was found that birds forced to go over the hurdles in order to keep up with the moving model later attained higher imprinting scores than control birds. In another experiment Hess induced his ducklings to follow a model up an inclined plane, and again found that the intensity of imprinting rose with the effort expended by the birds.

These results were said by Hess to conform to what he named the law of effort. He went so far as to formulate mathematically the relationship between the effort expended, $E$, and the strength of imprinting, $Is$: viz., $Is = \log E$. On a later occasion Hess carried out a further experiment to confirm the law of effort. The apparatus consisted of two identical stationary model ducks three feet apart; when the loudspeaker in either model was sounded this model was momentarily illuminated. By alternating the conjoined light and sound between the two decoys, it was possible to get a duckling to move to and fro between them. Ducklings were run at four and at sixteen shuttles, and Hess (1959a, 1959c) found that the subjects that had covered more ground were more strongly imprinted than those that had travelled less.

The interpretation of Hess's findings is open to doubt. For instance, it would appear that in the last experiment, subjects that had travelled more, also acquired more experience of the models. Therefore, this more extensive experience, rather than the extra effort, could have been the cause of the increased intensity of imprinting. Again, consider the finding that the more ground that was covered by the animals, the stronger was their attachment to the object. In these experiments, the more firmly imprinted subjects had followed the faster-moving object; it is not impossible that the faster-moving model provided more effective stimulation that the slower-moving one; and this factor alone could have been responsible for the more effective imprinting. Salzen and Sluckin (1959b) were unable to find any relation between the distance covered by their chicks on first exposure to a moving box and the performances of the chicks on subsequent occasions. However, the more fundamental question which remained unanswered was whether imprinting would be possible at all with only a minimum of movement on the part of the subject.

This is the problem to which Baer and Gray (1960) addressed themselves. They exposed individually thirty-two domestic chicks to a guinea pig, separated from the chick-compartment by a glass wall. Bodily contact with the guinea pig and overt following were prevented, both during the twenty-four hour exposure and during the test some days later which consisted of a choice between the familiar guinea pig and a strange one. Both the familiar and the strange guinea pigs could be white or black. The investigators found that their chicks discriminated, on the whole, in favour of the familiar guinea pigs, spending significantly more time beside them than beside the unfamiliar ones. It is, of course, conceivable that a chick could only develop an attachment to a guinea pig if it exerted some effort to approach and follow it. It is difficult to see how such exertions could be measured. In the circumstances it is improbable that effort rather than exposure to stimulation brought about imprinting to the guinea pigs in this experiment.

An attempt to put the law-of-effort hypothesis to test under conditions resembling closely the more usual laboratory imprinting procedures was made by Moltz, Rosenblum and Stettner (1960). In one of their experiments ducklings were placed, one at a time, in a small enclosure, permitting an unobstructed view of the moving object, but entirely preventing any following. In this way, the effort, or energy expended during exposure, was meant to be kept in the experimental subjects at a relatively low level. Control subjects were allowed to follow the model freely. Each duckling, whether restricted or unrestricted, was exposed to the moving object for twenty-five minutes per day for three days. On a subsequent test of following no difference in performance was found between the experimental and control animals. Thus, movement of the subject did not appear to help imprinting.

In this connection, Moltz and his colleagues also tested ducklings for stimulus generalisation. Experimental subjects were individually exposed to a moving object, but were prevented from following it, while control subjects were allowed to follow the object; all were then individually tested for following a new object. The experimental animals responded poorly to the new object; but so did the control animals. The extent of stimulus generalisation did not appear to depend on whether the training consisted only of exposure to stimulation, or of actually following the moving object.

Moltz (1963) also set out to test the rôle of movement in imprinting in another way. He placed ducklings in wooden stocks to restrict their movements, and then exposed them individually, some to a moving object (retreating, approaching, or both) and others to a stationary one. The animals became imprinted despite the restriction of their movement. The nature of the movement of the object made no difference to the extent of following on test, but ducklings which had been exposed to a stationary object followed less well. The experiment showed that, while movement of the subject was immaterial, movement of the object was important for imprinting.

The validity of the law of effort was questioned earlier by Moltz (1960) not only because together with his co-workers he failed to confirm Hess's hypothesis, but also because of some further available evidence against it. Thus, H. James was said to have conducted an unpublished experiment in which chicks were exposed to a flickering light, while not allowed to approach it. When allowed later to approach the light, these chicks did so as readily as the initially unrestricted control subjects. Again, Jaynes (1958a) found that imprinting could occur in chicks which, when originally exposed to a moving object, failed to follow it; he named this behaviour 'latent imprinting'.

Gottlieb (1961b) did not deliberately set out to test Hess's energy-expenditure hypothesis; he reported incidentally, however, that while his Peking ducklings were more vigorous initial followers than his mallard ducklings, yet the latter proved to be no less firmly imprinted by the discrimination criterion than the Peking ducklings. This finding would appear to run counter to expectations deriving from the hypothesis that following helps imprinting.

More recently Smith (1962) set out to test the law of effort in relation to approach responses of chicks. He placed each experimental chick in a small box restricting its movements, with the head protruding towards a flickering patch of light some distance away. These chicks were exposed in the course of two days for short periods of time to the flickering light; control chicks were similarly individually exposed to the light, but they were allowed to approach it. A day later all the chicks were tested individually for approach without any restriction. No significant differences were found in the behaviour of the two groups. Thus, the absence of movement during training sessions did not prevent the experimental chicks from becoming as well imprinted as those allowed freedom of movement in training. Smith also exposed chicks to a black-and-white rotating disc, preventing them by means of a transparent sheet of plastic from approaching the disc. He found that the growth of attachment of these chicks to the moving disc was unimpaired as compared with that of control chicks which had been free to approach the disc during training.

An experiment bearing somewhat on the problem of the rôle of the subject's effort in imprinting is that of Rice (1962). In this experiment some chicks followed freely a blue rubber ball emitting through a small loudspeaker a peeping noise, some were forced to follow it (they wore a small flexible collar connected to the ball by a twelve-inch string), and some, the control chicks, received no training. The training of the two experimental groups was during the first three days, and a discrimination test between the ball and a live hen took place on the fourth day. The untrained chicks somewhat preferred the hen while the others strongly preferred the ball; those chicks that had followed the ball freely performed significantly better than the chicks whose following had been forced. It is difficult to assume that the harnessed chicks expended less effort in following. It is possible that the effect of being pulled was a distraction which diminished the impact of the initial visual stimulation.

The view that energy expenditure by the subject is essential for imprinting has been given some support by studies of drug effects in imprinting situations. Drugs that are muscle relaxants, preventing muscular effort in training, could be thought to interfere with imprinting. Hess (1957) reported that meprobamate, a drug which prevents muscle tension, prevented the occurrence of imprinting in ducklings. Hess, Polt and Goodwin (1959) studied the effects of another tension reducing drug, carisoprodol, on imprinting in chicks and ducklings. It was concluded that carisoprodol, like meprobamate, interfered with imprinting; see also Hess, 1962.

It may be wondered why animals imprinted earlier have been found to perform normally under the influence of these drugs. Meprobamate in Hess's study did not, in fact, interfere with movement and motor co-ordination. Another drug, chlorpromazine, which Hess used, was found not to interfere with the process of imprinting; yet later studies reported that this drug interfered with motor activity (cf. survey in Sluckin and Salzen, 1961). Relatively little is known, as yet, about the various effects of the drugs used; it is, therefore, doubtful whether studies of performance under the influence of these drugs can help test Hess's theory concerning the rôle of effort in imprinting. However this may be, evidence seems to be accumulating at present which makes this theory, in its original form, untenable.

### (ii) The home environment

The first stage of imprinting, as it was originally understood, consisted of approach and following responses. As these are responses to intermittent stimulation, the implication was that young precocial birds could only become imprinted to sources of intermittent stimulation. Since stationary figures do not commonly elicit approach-and-stay responses, it was thought unlikely that imprinting to stationary objects would be possible. Attachment to home environment would have been thought to result from conditioning, but Thorpe (1956) suggested that such attachments could be acquired by a process akin to imprinting.

Gray (1960) set out to discover if chicks could become attached to motionless objects, prominently displayed in the visual environment. He exposed chicks individually to black geometrical figures (some chicks – to a circle, and some – to a triangle) for twenty-four hours, either during the third, or the fourth, or the fifth day of life. Each chick was in visual isolation from other chicks or any moving objects before the trial. Each chick was tested for fifteen minutes immediately after the trial for choice between the familiar and the unfamiliar figures. The results were clear: chicks tended to approach, and stay close to, the figures experienced earlier. Thus Gray showed that imprinting with static figures did occur. No doubt, intermittent visual stimulation resulting from flicker or movement imprints itself far more readily upon the animal than static stimulation. Nevertheless, it looks as if 'retinal flicker' is not a necessary condition of imprinting.

James (1961) suggested that the effect obtained by Gray might depend on a mechanism other than that which brings about imprinting to moving objects and flicker. The ability to become attached to a stationary object tended in Gray's experiment to increase with age: the most firmly attached chicks were the ones exposed to the goemetrical figures during the fifth day of life. Attachments to intermittent visual stimulation are often strongest when formed much earlier than the fifth day. Further, Abercrombie and James (1961) found that although their chicks did approach some stationary objects and stayed near them, such approach fixation required a very much greater number of trials than approach fixation to localised intermittent light.

However, various indications of attachment to stationary figures have been repeatedly reported in chicks under laboratory conditions. Thus, James (1959) mentioned the tendency in his chicks to spend more time in the half of the runway in which there was a polythene ball rather than in the empty half. Again, Hess (1959c) reported that three-day old chicks spent more time near a geometrical form, a circle or a triangle, to which they had been exposed during the day before the test, than near an unfamiliar figure.

Recently, Taylor & Taylor* reared newly hatched chicks in individual pens, with either a cardboard box or a piece of foam rubber hanging against one of the walls. After two days each subject was tested in a runway where both objects were available. A significant proportion of chicks approached the object with which they had been reared. In many cases the animals pecked and rubbed against the familiar object, giving contentment calls.

Abercrombie and James (1961) hinted that a preference for familiar figures might result from the extra discriminability and attention-getting value acquired by these figures. Now, it is an established fact that rats reared in the presence of certain geometrical patterns could later learn to discriminate among these patterns more readily than rats reared without previously being exposed to them (cf. Gibson and Walk, 1956; Gibson, Walk, Pick and Tighe, 1958; Walk, Gibson, Pick and Tighe, 1959). However, it is not quite clear how the tendency to form attachments and readiness to learn discrimination tasks, both of which depend on exposure to appropriate stimulation, are inter-related.

Attachments to stationary objects constituting the environment of the animal were inferred from certain observations of the behaviour of domestic chicks by Sluckin (1960, 1962) and Sluckin and Salzen (1961). Now it may be readily observed that a naïve chick placed in a runway with a moving object will sooner or later start following the object, will continue to do so vigorously for some hours, will then gradually abandon the pursuit, and will finally cease following the object altogether. If food and water are provided in one part of the runway, the chick will tend to spend more and more time in that part. If, when the chick no longer follows the moving object, a strange object, moving or stationary, is introduced into the runway, then the chick will again start following the original object. Even when the change in the static environment is made 'behind the chick's back', the chick will re-commence following the moving object as soon as the change catches its attention. Such restoration of following may be

---

* I am grateful to my colleagues Ann Taylor and Keith Taylor for this report of 'imprinting to a static feature of the home environment'.

equally easily brought about by placing the chick together with its moving object in another, strange runway.

The chick's return to the familiar moving object shows that it recognises the strangeness of its environment. The chick behaves as if it feared the strange situation, attempting to flee from it by reverting to the proximity of the familiar object. Fear responses will be considered at length in Chapter 7. We shall then see that the animal's responses to environmental disturbances can be taken to indicate the existence of an imprinting-like attachment of the animal to its 'home'.

### (iii) Imprinting and domestication

Following mother and becoming imprinted to her must be of enormous survival value to the young, especially the young of wild species. Becoming attached to members of the species as such, could also be of great advantage to the individual. While it has been amply demonstrated that staying with parents is a result of imprinting, imprinting may also be responsible, at least in part, for flocking, such as, for instance, the tendency of young wild geese and ducks to stay together even when they are physically capable of dispersal. In domestic birds, however, attachment of the young to adults, and flocking, would appear to be less important for survival than in wild species.

Klopfer (1956) went so far as to suggest that susceptibility to imprinting could be a maladaptive trait in domestic animals because of 'a high likelihood of the occurrence of imprinting onto wrong objects'. Klopfer thought that imprintability would tend to be a 'labile trait' in domestic species, and that this could account for the great individual differences in the intensity of approach and following responses and the ability to form attachments reported by various investigators.

The interesting suggestion that there might be differences between wild and domesticated animals in their imprintability was taken up by Gottlieb (1961b). Gottlieb chose for his investigation two races of the common duck: the mallard, a wild representative of the species, and the Peking duck, one of the domestic varieties. The experimental animals were individually exposed for twenty minutes to a silent, papier-maché duck decoy moving in a circular runway. They were all individually tested for discrimination between male and female models at twenty-seven to thirty hours after hatching. The initial following responses turned out to be more prominent in the domestic ducklings than in the young mallards. Actual imprinting was about equally strong in the domestic, the wild, and some semi-wild ducks.

Gottlieb concluded that his findings were contrary to the hypothesis of maladaptation of imprinting under domestication.

Similarities in the behaviour of wild and domesticated birds were stressed earlier by Collias (1952). The retention of filial responsiveness and imprintability in domestic species may have been due to the value of these tendencies for successful breeding (see Gottlieb, 1961b). However, as we saw in the last chapter, the rôle of imprinting in bringing the sexes together is still rather uncertain.

While some people have wondered whether imprinting declines under conditions of domestication, others* have suggested that imprinting actually helps domestication. This is difficult to countenance. Wild animals learned to follow man probably because this was rewarding, and not because man was a moving figure, attractive in itself, to the young. Domestication continued later to be enhanced by selective breeding for docility. The only safe conclusion, tentative as it must be, is that domestication and imprinting are not essentially related.

* For instance, M. Burton in a note in *Daily Telegraph*, December, 1962.

# Chapter 6

# THE SENSITIVE PERIOD

## (i) Sensitive and critical periods

Imprinting has been said to occur during a specifiable period early in the life of the individual. This period is referred to as the sensitive period because it has been noted that at that particular time exposure to certain stimulus configurations leads to the formation of attachments to them. This period is also known as the critical period because it has been said that at no other time imprinting attachments may be formed; and it has been thought that if imprinting does not then occur, it will never occur. Although a sensitive period need not necessarily be critical, it has been assumed that the sensitive period for imprinting is its critical period.

It is not, of course, a new notion that there may be periods in onto-genetic development during which any individual is particularly sensitive or impressionable, when particular experiences exert a profound and lasting influence on the individual's later behaviour. Freud, for instance, postulated several distinct stages in human psycho-sexual development during which experiences of different kinds could lead to fixations and thus mould human character. In other words, highly specific patterns of behaviour are, according to the psycho-analytic view, acquired by each individual at each of these developmental stages. Similarly, Murphy (1947) implied that there must be periods critical in the personality development of any human being; he suggested that during certain times general needs develop into specific needs according to the particular experiences of the given individual at those times, and these determine his tastes and idiosyncrasies for his life-time.

It has not been easy to confirm the existence of such truly critical stages in the development of human beings. However, in the case of other mammals some precise observations have indicated that certain periods in ontogeny are indeed of crucial importance for the development of some characteristic behaviour-patterns. Thus, Scott (1945) reported that a female lamb raised on the bottle for the first ten days of its life, remained isolated from the flock, was attached to people, and later made a poor mother. This and some later observations (cf. Scott, Fredericson and Fuller, 1951) have shown that there is a critical period, starting almost at birth for some aspects of social and 'personality' development in sheep (Scott, 1962). Similarly, Scott (1958b) reported a critical period in the social development of dogs (see also Scott and Marston, 1950). Scott suggests that the social relationship established between puppies and their human masters may be similar to that which normally exists between offspring and parents.

The time between the third and the seventh week after birth has been found by Scott and his co-investigators to be the only time when puppies are capable of forming lasting attachments to people, or to their own kind. Harlow and Harlow (1962) report that young rhesus monkeys form strong social bonds among themselves between the third and the sixth month of life; social deprivation during that time is said to damage their ability ever to achieve a satisfactory 'social adjustment'.

Scott (1958a, 1958b) considers that during the critical period of 'primary socialisation' the young animal becomes attached to a group of animals which normally consists of members of its own species; but during that period a tie to another species can be experimentally or accidentally established. A young animal can also form a social bond both with its own and with other species: thus, puppies that have had early contact with dogs and people tend to become attached to both.

Leaving aside for the present any consideration of the character of this early learning (see Chapter 8), it may be noted that Scott (1962) holds that critical periods are of the utmost importance in determining the social, emotional and even intellectual development of any individual. Like Lorenz, Scott invokes the embryological analogy in stressing the importance of critical learning. Just as the early organisation of cells in the embryo determines once and for all the later anatomical structure, so early learning determines later behaviour and inhibits any subsequent re-patterning of behaviour.

Others concerned with the study of early learning are less inclined to ascribe such criticality to the sensitive period. Hinde (1962a) points out that the sensitive period is never sharply defined; it is often an optimal period for learning rather than a critical one. And it is not a period that is circumscribed solely by physical maturation; for its range is determined by the impact of the environment upon the developing organism (cf. Schneirla, 1956; Moltz, 1960; Sluckin, 1962).

There are probably optimal periods in the development of children for learning to speak or to read, for learning to walk, for susceptibility to traumas associated with separation from mother-figure, and so on. Animals are even more apt to learn certain forms of behaviour when young, or miss learning them altogether (e.g. Forgays and Read, 1962; see also review by Levine, 1962a). However, the most critical learning period of all has appeared to be that for imprinting. It is also the one about which there is a great deal of well-attested observational evidence.

Before considering the experimental findings concerning the critical period for imprinting, it is useful to distinguish between (1) the time between the onset and disappearance of approach and following responses, and (2) the sensitive period for imprinting. For it is not impossible that at some developmental stages approach and following will not result in imprinting to the objects of these responses, while at other times approach and following will lead to exclusive attachments. Some investigators have tacitly assumed that so long as the animal shows readiness to approach and follow, it is also capable of forming attachments to the objects of these responses, and when the animal ceases to be responsive it also ceases to be capable of becoming imprinted. At any rate, some studies have been primarily concerned with the onset and waning of initial filial responses, while others have explicitly set out to investigate the critical period of imprinting.

### (ii) The time of approach and following

The early reports concerning the time when approach and following responses could be evoked in young nidifugous birds were about wild species: the coot and various species of wild duck. Alley and Boyd (1950) found that coot chicks would respond to calls made by people and readily follow people until about eight hours after hatching. This 'tameness' was found to disappear by the second day of life. Alley and Boyd apparently believed that by that time imprinting was complete.

Young coots, as well as young moorhens, were later the subjects of extensive investigations by Hinde, Thorpe and Vince (1956). These

6

investigators found that young coots would become attracted to a moving object even when first confronted with the object as late as six days after hatching. Young moorhens were much more adversely affected than coots by the delay in being presented with the first opportunity to follow; at six days of age moorhens did not respond when tested with a moving object. One of the conclusions drawn was that the time limits of the sensitive period applied primarily to the initial elicitation of the following responses rather than to imprintability or learning capacity.

Earlier Fabricius (1951b) reported that in three species of duck maximal following occurred at about twelve hours after hatching. He also found that auditory stimuli acted longer as releasers of following than visual stimuli; that is, ducklings were still ready to respond to sound signals when they were no longer sensitive to visual signals. Fabricius and Boyd (1954) reported that, while the period at which following could first be elicited was not very sharply defined, the highest proportion of followers among mallard ducklings at first testing was at ages ranging from twenty-five hours to fifty hours, although the majority would follow a silent model at any age from three to seventy-two hours after hatching. While Lorenz (1935) thought that in mallard ducklings the sensitive period was confined to the first few hours of life, Fabricius and Boyd (1954) found that approach and following responses could be evoked in some naïve young mallards even at ten days of age; see also Fabricius (1962).

Experimenting with domestic chicks, Jaynes (1957) investigated the incidence of their responsiveness to a moving figure at various ages. These chicks had been housed collectively until the time of testing, which consisted of exposing each chick to a moving object. The subject's approach and following responses were assessed during the last five minutes of a thirty-minute session. Only a few chicks were tested at each age reckoned in hours after hatching. The youngest chicks were the most responsive, but the total numbers were too small to indicate reliably the modal age of optimal responsiveness. Delays of up to fifty-four hours in exposure to the moving object did not prevent some chicks from responding to it positively. However, none of the eight chicks tested between fifty-four and sixty hours after hatching approached or followed the moving object.

A complicating factor in this study lay in the fact that the five-minute test was preceded in each case by a two-minute stoppage in the movement of the object. Thus, the test which we have classified as a test of initial responsiveness may also be regarded as a recognition test, or one of short-term retention. And Jaynes himself fully recognised the difference between the critical period for the elicitation of following and one for imprinting proper. His findings, in brief, were that (1) the incidence of approach and following is highest in the first six hours or so after hatching, and (2) that this period of responsiveness ends some time during the third day of the chick's life.

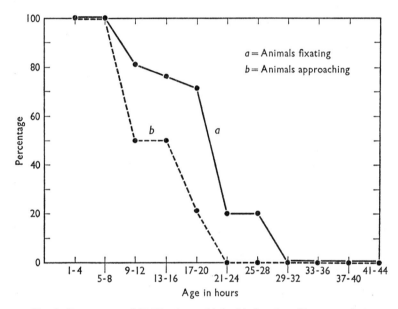

*Fig. 5: Percentage of 124 Leghorn chicks (a) fixating, (b) approaching the stimulus object at different ages (from Hess and Schaefer, 1959)*

In this context the responsiveness of domestic chicks to sound was investigated by Hess and Schaefer (1959). Their experimental design was straight-forward: naïve chicks were individually confronted for two minutes with a model emitting a rhythmical repetition of a sound made by a human voice. Among the several features of behaviour noted were (a) the chick's orientation (fixation), and (b) approach towards the model. The results are shown in Fig. 5. The incidence of approach was found to be 100 per cent among the chicks up to eight hours post-hatch; very little responsiveness was found after the first day of life; thus, under the conditions of the investigation the sensitive period for aural stimuli ended relatively early.

Instead of using intermittent sound as the initial releasing stimulus, intermittent light could be used for this purpose. James (1960a) found that the tendency to approach such a light source at first exposure was stronger in chicks up to twenty-four hours old than in chicks seven days old. But it is of great interest that these older chicks still remained responsive.

Gray (1962) tested the responsiveness of domestic chicks of different ages to a hen. He found that the responsiveness of 'naïve' chicks tended to fluctuate, a steady decline setting in after about four days of age.

The results of the various studies need not be regarded as conflicting. For the period during which the initial approach and following responses may be elicited depends on the experimental species, the nature of the stimuli employed, and – as we shall see later – the conditions under which the animals are kept.

### (iii)  The critical time for imprinting

The critical period for imprinting is most decisively determined by putting young animals that have earlier been 'trained' at various ages to a test of preference between familiar and strange figures. The training ages of those animals that later 'pass' the test indicate the imprinting age span, and the ages of the animals that later 'fail' the test are outside the critical period for imprinting. Strictly, the actual behaviour of the young animal during training is irrelevant to the determination of the imprinting critical period. Only the test performance on a later occasion can indicate whether the animal has become imprinted as a result of the earlier training session.

Ramsay and Hess (1954) set out to determine the critical period for imprinting in mallard ducklings. Ducklings of various ages were given individually either ten minutes or thirty minutes training with a travelling model of a mallard drake, fitted with a heating element and emitting a particular series of calls. Then, on a later occasion, any time from five to seventy hours after training, each duckling was tested in four stages for choice between the familiar model and a model of a female mallard emitting the recorded voice of a mallard duck calling her young. The choice of the male model was taken as evidence of imprinting. Using in all ninety-two ducklings, and plotting 'perfect' imprinting test scores against age, the investigators found the critical period to range from five to twenty-four hours after hatching with an optimum at thirteen to sixteen hours, as shown in Fig. 6. The limits of the critical period were wider by a less stringent criterion of imprinting, a less-than-perfect preference for the familiar model.

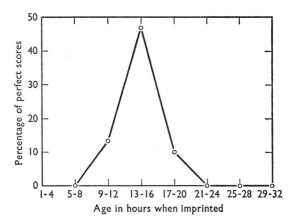

Fig. 6: Percentage for 'perfect' scores for mallards imprinted in various age groups (from Ramsay and Hess, 1954)

The critical period for imprinting in domestic Peking ducklings was thoroughly investigated by Gottlieb (1961a). He gave his subjects twenty-minute training sessions with a model of a mallard drake.

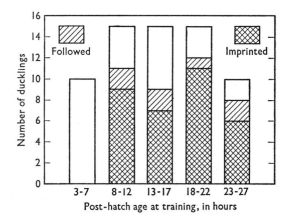

Fig. 7: Occurrence of following and imprinting during testing as a function of post-hatch age at training (from Gottlieb, 1961a)

Different groups of subjects were trained at ages varying from three to twenty-seven hours after hatching. Later each duckling was tested at twenty-seven to thirty hours after hatching for choice between the familiar decoy and another of a mallard duck. The results are summarized in Fig. 7. The white areas in the figure correspond to the numbers of subjects that did not follow either of the two decoys on test; the lightly shaded areas show the numbers that followed either both decoys or the strange decoy only; the heavily shaded areas show

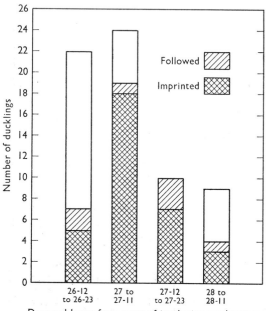

*Fig. 8: Occurrence of following and imprinting during testing as a function of developmental age at training (from Gottlieb, 1961a)*

the numbers of subjects that chose the familiar figure and were therefore considered imprinted. It will be noted that the critical period for imprinting extended in this study from eight hours to somewhere beyond twenty-seven hours post-hatch.

There was no clearly-marked peak time, in terms of post-hatch ages, within the critical period for imprinting. Gottlieb (1961a) went on to consider the critical period in terms of ages calculated from the onset of incubation. The age counted from the onset of incubation was called by Gottlieb 'developmental age'; and the ducklings in the experiment hatched out at various developmental ages, on the twenty-sixth and twenty-seventh day of incubation. Figure 8 shows the occurrence of imprinting in terms of incubation age. The critical period stands out at the developmental age of twenty-seven days. It would appear that the critical period for imprinting might be more sharply defined in terms of developmental age than in terms of conventional age.

Using the same way of defining the critical period, Gottlieb and Klopfer (1962) found that the optimal time for imprinting ducklings visually occurred a little later than the best time for auditory imprinting. Probably the extent of the critical period depends on the effectiveness of the stimulus figure. For relatively poor stimulation the critical period would be expected to be of shorter duration than for highly effective stimulation. A quantitative investigation of the relationship between the character of the stimuli and the critical period for imprinting could be worth while.

### (iv) Restriction of exposure to stimulation

The evidence considered so far seems conclusive in indicating that the period early in the life of precocial birds when they respond to suitable stimulation by approach and following, and when they are imprintable, is a strictly limited one. And yet, investigators have observed that their experimental subjects sometimes remained responsive well beyond the usual critical period. Fabricius and Boyd (1954), for instance, reported that one of the six ducklings that had been kept apart from other ducklings followed a model when first faced with it at 10 days of age. Salzen and Sluckin (1959b) found that some of their chicks remained ready to follow a moving box on first presentation up to the age of five days and sometimes longer. What, then, are the circumstances which bring about this extension of the traditionally reported relatively short critical period?

As we have seen in Chapter 4, Guiton (1958) seems to have been the first to note the precise conditions which affect the readiness of young precocial birds to approach and follow moving objects. He found that chicks raised in a group would follow a moving object up to the end of the third day of life, but not thereafter. On the other hand, chicks raised in visual isolation from one another, from other animals, and from people, would still approach and follow moving objects after the third day. The reason for this – Guiton (1959) suggested – was that chicks reared in isolation were unimprinted when tested. They remained responsive to moving figures without any discrimination at a time when communally reared chicks were not. Under conditions of group rearing, chicks soon became imprinted to one another, and after two or three days approached only their own kind, and not any new figures.

James (1960a) reported that, even when seven days old, chicks exposed for the first time to an intermittent light source would approach it. It should be noted that these chicks had been kept in visual isolation from one another except for a short early period. James (1960b) also reported that chicks that had been given ample opportunity to become attached to one another were attracted less by a flickering light than chicks that had been reared apart from one another from the age of about two days; the difference in responsiveness between these two groups became very considerable from the fifth day after hatching. Sluckin and Salzen (1961) found that none of their socially reared chicks followed a moving object when first confronted with it at the age of five or six days, but a third of the chicks they had reared in isolation did so.

It is clear that the first appearance of approach and following responses depends on the opportunity afforded by the presence of intermittent stimulation. If a moving figure or a flickering light source are presented to a precocial bird very early in its life, and if this animal has a chance to form an attachment to the given type of visual stimulation, then it will not thereafter approach or follow other stimulus sources. If, however, the opportunity to approach and follow does not present itself until a little later in the animal's life, then the capacity to respond positively to any intermittent visual stimulation is retained longer. Thus, it looks as if the very process of imprinting could bring about the end of the period of general responsiveness (Sluckin and Salzen, 1961).

This theory could be further tested by reducing in various ways the earliest visual experiences of young birds with a view to finding out if this would extend the critical period for approach and following responses and imprinting. Moltz and Stettner (1961) expected such an effect because they rejected the earlier notion of a critical period as a function of maturational events only. These investigators, in keeping with the views of Schneirla (1959) and following Moltz (1960), supposed that the duration of the critical period would depend upon the impact of sensory experiences upon the maturing organism.

Moltz and Stettner (1961) reduced the early visual experiences of ducklings in an experimental group by fitting the animals with hoods which allowed diffuse light to reach the subjects' eyes but prevented perception of visual form. Each duckling was kept in a cage until the time when it was placed without its hood in the alley containing a moving box. This trial consisted of a twenty-five-minute exposure to the test object, the hoodless animal then spent a day in its cage, and finally it was given another twenty-five-minute trial. Different sub-groups of the experimental animals were exposed for the first time to the moving object at twelve hours, twenty-four hours, forty-eight hours and seventy-two hours after hatching. Control animals were

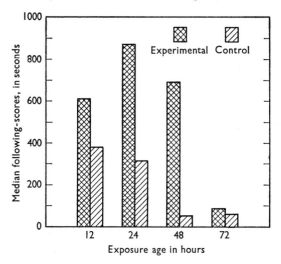

*Fig. 9: Median following-scores obtained by experimental and control Ss after different exposure ages (from Moltz and Stettner, 1961)*

treated in exactly the same way except that their hoods had holes in them permitting normal vision. The results are set out in Fig. 9. The following-score for each subject was based on the two trials. It was clear that the period of responsiveness could be appreciably extended by preventing any experience of patterned-light before exposure to intermittent visual stimulation.

It should be noted that the loss of general responsiveness in socially reared birds is not necessarily a permanent one. Guiton (1958, 1959) showed that socially reared chicks, subsequently kept in isolation, often respond all the more vigorously to *any* moving object. In one sense, therefore, their initial imprinting was highly reversible. Thus, a limited amount of visual experience could lead to extensive stimulus generalisation and an enhancement of general responsiveness.

How far may the critical period be extended by an initial restriction of exposure to stimulation? As mentioned in Chapter 4, Baron and Kish (1960) reared some chicks in complete social isolation for the first four weeks of their lives. These chicks were then tested for reactivity to a 'stimulus animal' and were found to be relatively unresponsive; see also Baron, Kish and Antonitis (1961).

Sluckin (1962) trained singly reared chicks for some hours with a moving object for the first time at the age of eight days, and later tested them at fifteen days of age for discrimination between the familiar object and a strange one. These chicks 'passed' the test, showing that they could be imprinted at a late age, previously considered to be well outside the critical period. However, when isolated chicks were first exposed to a moving object at the age of fifteen days, they were found later to be hardly at all imprinted to the object. So it looks as if imprintability to new stimulus configurations diminishes with age even when early imprinting has been prevented.

On the other hand there are some indications that imprinting could occur in older precocial birds. It will be remembered that in the experiment conducted by Baron and Kish (1960) the chicks that had been initially reared in isolation until the age of four weeks were subsequently kept from the fifth to the tenth week of life in a communal cage. These chicks were, thus, given the first opportunity to become attached to one another at a relatively late age. In fact, when these chicks were individually tested at the age of ten weeks they spent as much time near the 'stimulus animal' – an age mate – as did the controls which had been with their own kind all their lives. As mentioned earlier, it is possible that the gregariousness which the experimental chicks developed between the fifth and tenth weeks of life was in some measure due to imprinting. It is, however, clear that this gregariousness could also have developed as a result of instrumental learning; for staying close to age mates might lead a chick to a variety of rewards, such as warmth, shelter, food and water.

Now in a later experiment Baron, Kish and Antonitis (1962) reared groups of domestic chicks under three conditions during the first ten weeks of life: (a) communal, (b) communal for one week, followed by nine weeks of isolation, and (c) isolation for one week, followed by nine weeks of communical experience. Tests of 'social reactivity' to a 'stimulus animal' were conducted at five weeks and at ten weeks after hatching. It was found that the effects of early isolation or early social contact were greatly modified by subsequent experiences, and the conclusion that emerged was that, while much social learning occurred very early in life, social learning occurred also at later developmental stages. The possibility of imprinting playing some part in this later social learning could not be excluded.

Waller and Waller (1963) thought that imprinting was not the basis of later aggregative behaviour because the ducklings that they had raised in isolation flocked together after a period of confinement in close quarters. There can be no certainty, however, that such attachments, even when acquired late in life, do not derive in some measure from imprinting. All that can be said about these experimental findings is that the importance of social learning was manifest at all stages of ontogeny rather than at the earliest stages only.

It is interesting to note that Harlow (1958) reported that filial attachments of young monkeys to surrogate 'mothers', while normally acquired very early in life, could also develop at the comparatively late age of eight months. This late adoption of 'cloth mothers' appeared to develop in the usual way, without any extraneous positive reinforcement. Harlow remarked that although such late adoptions might take place, the intensity of affectional responses was diminished by the delay in the exposure to the tactual and other stimuli provided by the 'cloth mother'.

What can be concluded from all this about the critical period? In precocial birds aggregative behaviour is learned; and this learning is not always restricted to any special period. The available evidence makes it clear that when social learning occurs very early in life, then what takes place is unreinforced imprinting rather than reward conditioning (cf., Taylor and Sluckin, 1964a). When social learning occurs later, then it may or it may not contain an element of imprinting. If imprinting could be shown to be a factor in later social learning, then the notion of the relatively short, early critical period would have to be abandoned. However, there is so far no conclusive evidence that in precocial birds the capacity for imprinting can persist, even under the most favourable circumstances, beyond the juvenile stage of development.

### (v) The termination of the sensitive period

A number of views have been put forward or implied to explain the termination of the sensitive period for the approach and following responses, and the imprinting of these responses. Kaufman and Hinde (1961) have classified the theories into four categories; these we may conveniently list and name as follows: (1) the maturational end of sensitivity, (2) inhibition through socialisation, (3) the growth of timidity, and (4) the end of the state of low anxiety.

The first of these theories suggests that the tendency to approach and follow naturally wanes as the animal grows older, and that this waning is internally determined, rather than due to any impact of experiences. Such an explanation of the relative shortness of the critical period was implicit in the original accounts of imprinting given by Lorenz (1935) and by Fabricius (1951a).

This view, very broadly interpreted, can hardly be refuted. For it is difficult to conceive any experiments or observations which could show conclusively that there is *no* waning of responsiveness other than as a result of experience. Narrowly interpreted, however, the theory of the maturational end of the sensitive period has been entirely discredited by the finding that an early end of the critical period can be prevented by restricting the animal's early exposure to stimulation. (Guiton, 1958, 1959; James, 1960a,b; Sluckin and Salzen, 1961; Moltz and Stettner, 1961).

Thus the second theory, that imprintability to new objects is largely inhibited by socialisation, seems plausible. It calls, however, for some reformulation. In the light of the available evidence it may be said that the sensitive period for imprinting tends to continue so long as no firm imprinting has taken place. Imprinting of the approach and following responses to any stimulus configuration tends to inhibit approach and imprinting to new figures (Sluckin and Salzen, 1961).

The third theory suggests that the close of the sensitive period is caused by the development of fearfulness (Hinde, 1955b). On this view the growth of fear responses finally inhibits approach and following responses; cf. Hinde, Thorpe and Vince (1956) and Hess (1957, 1959a,b, 1962b). This explanation of the termination of the critical period for imprinting has had quite a wide acceptance; see, for instance, Candland and Campbell (1962), Waller and Waller (1963) and Hersher, Richmond and Moore (1963). Much of the next chapter is concerned with the problems posed by the fear theory.

At this stage, however, it is worth recalling that it has been observed that in some cases the following responses waned in the absence of any indication of fear (Jaynes, 1956; Weidmann, 1956, 1958); and the view that the escape tendency caused the termination of the critical period was, according to Weidmann (1958) untenable in the case of mallards. Weidmann was inclined to believe that the maturation of the escape tendency could be a factor contributing to the termination of the critical period, but not the sole cause of it. Sluckin and Salzen (1961) pointed out later that fear itself could be in some ways a consequence of imprinting (see Chapter 7).

As Kaufman and Hinde (1961) stress, the concept of a well-defined critical period is rather misleading. What many investigators have established is 'a gradual change in the probability that imprinting will occur, depending on both the conditions of rearing and the test procedure'. The onset and end of the critical period certainly cannot be clearly defined in terms of post-hatch age. But, at least in the case of the Peking duck, a relatively well-defined critical period has been shown to exist in terms of developmental age, i.e. age calculated from the onset of incubation (Gottlieb, 1961a). This indicates that 'readiness for imprinting wanes on the basis of maturational factors alone'. Gottlieb appears to go further than Weidmann in criticising the view that the onset of fear puts an end to imprintability. For the young of the highly domesticated Peking duck generally show little fear; therefore, it is unlikely that a general flight tendency plays a crucial part in terminating imprintability, at least in the tame species.

Now, fear and its relation to imprinting are examined more fully in the next chapter. So is the concept of anxiety, and in particular the fourth of the theories listed earlier, advanced by Moltz (1960), which suggests that the critical period for imprinting ends when the state of low intensity of 'anxiety drive' ends. To clarify the rôle of fear and anxiety in ending the sensitive period, it will be necessary (a) to examine the present state of knowledge concerning the ontogenetic development of fear responses, and (b) to look into the character of theorising which invokes the concept of anxiety.

Chapter 7

# FEAR AND ANXIETY

### (i) The development of timidity

The term, fear, refers in everyday language to a particular emotional experience, the behavioural concomitants of which include response of immobility or flight, changes in breathing and sphincter control, etc. Fear may be brought about 'either by sudden and intense stimulation or by specific classes of stimuli that must be identified empirically for each species studied' (Verplanck, 1957). No doubt, such specific classes of stimuli are determinable for any one individual; but it is somewhat uncertain to what extent they are susceptible to identification for a species as a whole.

What specific classes of stimuli does a chick or a duckling fear? Spalding (1873) observed that chicks might approach and follow a human hand at one stage of their development and run away from it at another. Fabricius (1951a), and later Ramsay and Hess (1954), noted that objects which could evoke fear responses in ducklings could also elicit approach and following. And Hinde, Thorpe and Vince (1956) found that this was so also in the case of young moorhens and coots. On occasions the tendency to approach and follow a figure appears to be disturbed by the tendency to flee from it. And at times fear responses appear to inhibit entirely any incipient approach and following responses to a given figure. This may be so in one individual and not in another, or in the same individual at one time and not at another time.

Observations have been made on young birds seemingly in a state of conflict, being at once 'attracted' and 'repelled' by the same figure. Young chicks can sometimes be seen approaching a moving object, backing away from it, approaching it again, and so on. Sometimes the animal stands still while the moving object passes near-by; the young bird moves its head a little towards the object, then away from it, then towards it again, repeating these head movements several times.

Such vacillation may be seen when an animal which is being imprinted to object A is also somewhat attracted by object B; as imprinting to A continues, the animal becomes ambivalent about B, finally fleeing from it (Hinde, 1961). Some ambivalence has also been seen in chicks which initially would flee from a moving object presented to them; but after some trials spread over several days such an animal would take to following the object, though running away momentarily, whenever too close to it. In one such case the chick lost its fear, and started to follow unequivocally a moving box, only on the fourteenth day of its life; when subsequently tried day after day for some days, it continued following the box (Sluckin and Salzen, 1961).

It has been said that newly hatched precocial birds are fearless. Thus, Spalding (1873) thought that fear did not show itself in domestic chicks until the third day of life, and then developed rapidly between the third and the fourth day. Subsequent reports concerning the onset of timidity have been somewhat conflicting. One tentative statement may be found in an article by Gray and Howard (1957); these investigators concluded that fear in chicks was at its maximum between the third and fifth day after hatching, and then started to decline.

A systematic study of the development of avoidance behaviour in gallinaceous birds and waterfowl was made by Schaller and Emlen (1962); the domestic fowl, turkey, Muscovy duck and Chinese goose were investigated, and among the wild species, three species of pheasant, the Japanese quail, the Eastern turkey and the mallard. Many of the young birds were kept in solitary confinement until testing for signs of fear, but others were reared in solid-walled boxes in pairs, or in boxes with windows, either alone or in pairs. The testing consisted simply of putting into the cage a rod with a card fixed to it right-angles. An initial retreat from the card was taken to indicate fear. The main finding was that under conditions of visual restriction there was a gradual rise in avoidance behaviour up to the age of from four to six days. Among other things it was also noted that birds reared in pairs showed more fear when tested from the second post-hatch day onwards than those reared singly.

Considering the well attested fact of a gradual rise in the level of timidity, the conclusion might seem inescapable that fear would interfere with, and sooner or later totally inhibit, any tendency to approach and follow (and become imprinted to) newly presented figures. And, as mentioned at the end of the last chapter, this was the view first put forward by Hinde, and later by Hess. However, in the light of the evidence about the development of fear in the young of the domestic fowl and related species available at present, it seems necessary to modify the earlier view concerning the relationship between imprinting and fear. How, then, does fear develop?

### (ii) Fear of figure and/or ground

In considering the development of fear reactions, it is convenient to distinguish between two aspects of the animal's environment which may be feared, (a) a fluctuating stimulus pattern, or figure, and (b) the static environment, or ground (Sluckin, 1960). Observations of fear referred to so far have been concerned with fear of moving objects, or figures. Sluckin and Salzen (1961) did, however, also consider indications in young birds of fear of the static environment. Salzen (1962) investigated systematically fear responses of chicks up to seven days of age, reared communally or singly, (1) to a static environment only – a runway with a stationary object in it – and (2) to an environment combining the stationary and fluctuating elements – a runway with a moving object, or a runway containing one or more chicks.

Salzen noted fear responses to new ground, in the form of 'freezing' and 'distress' calls, in chicks of all ages; the older chicks appeared also to attempt escape from the unfamiliar runway by jumping up at the walls. He concluded that the fear shown was a response to the strangeness of the runway. Schaller and Emlen (1962) maintained likewise that strangeness 'was the single essential stimulus property responsible for negative reponse'.

Salzen (1962) found that fear of the static environment did not greatly depend on whether chicks had been reared socially or in isolation. All chicks had a familiar perceptual world, and fear resulted from the contrast between this familiar environment and the strange new environment. It would appear that the degree of acceptance of any *new* ground is a function of exposure to it. Further, the longer the time spent in any one environment, the more relatively strange is any new environment. As Schaller and Emlen (1962) point out, it takes time to make things familiar, and thus time is needed before new things are perceived as strange. Since fear is a function of strangeness, fear develops with time.

As for the fear of a moving figure, Salzen (1962) essentially confirmed earlier findings about the following responses of chicks reared socially and chicks reared in isolation. Most isolated chicks, when confronted with a moving figure, showed at first signs of fear – freezing followed by distress calls – and in the case of older chicks, avoidance behaviour too. However, fear was within a few minutes replaced by positive responses to the moving object, coupled with contentment chirps. In the case of seven-day old chicks raised in isolation the change from an initial flight from, to a movement towards, the moving object was very marked.

Socially reared chicks showed more fear and less 'contentment' when tested for three minutes with a moving box during the second day of life. At three to four days of age socially reared chicks tested for the first time would sometimes switch from fear to 'pleasure responses as a result of continued experience of the moving object'. Guiton (1959) reported that chicks raised communally did not approach and follow a moving object after the age of three days. Salzen substantially confirmed this; unlike seven-day old chicks reared singly, socially reared seven-day old chicks could not be imprinted to a moving box.

When a young precocial bird is faced with a strange figure in a strange environment, its fear appears to be general. When only the figure is strange, the animal fears it, and if old enough, runs away from it. What if the figure is familiar and the ground strange? As we saw in Chapter 5, fear of the environment appears to 'push' the animal towards the figure.

While considering the evidence in support of the view that animals become attached to their environment in an imprinting-like manner, we noted that a change in the static environment made the manifestations of attachment to the familiar figure more evident and striking. Various forms of environmental disturbance, including loud unfamiliar noises, made imprinted chicks run towards, and follow closely, the familiar moving figure (Sluckin, 1960; Sluckin and Salzen, 1961). Guiton (1961), too, reported that imprinted chicks could often be 'forced' to keep closer to the model by being 'mildly scared' by the experimenter. He also found that when a group of chicks were in a runway together with a moving model, the chicks would frequently resume following the model when disturbed by noise from outside the runway. This change in behaviour could again be explained as being due to the fear of the changed auditory environment. Pitz and Ross

(1961) reported a similar finding; in their experiment, sudden intense noises were made whenever a chick came within some six inches of the stimulus object; in these circumstances the following of the object was significantly enhanced.

It is clear that while fear of the figure tends to inhibit approach and following, fear of the ground tends to stimulate these responses to the figure. Fear of any particular environment may develop in a variety of conditions. It may come about as a consequence of attachment to another environment; then other environments are feared because they are strange. Fear of environment may also be conditioned; the environment is then feared because it is associated with some stimulation which gives rise to discomfort or pain. However, no matter how the fear comes about, it may be expected that an animal fearing the environment would tend to move towards the figure.

This is borne out by the findings of Moltz, Rosenblum and Halikas (1959). These investigators kept ducklings individually with a moving box for twenty-five minutes per day, for ten days. Although these ducklings were not at any stage given a discrimination test, there is little doubt that the training was sufficient to imprint the ducklings to the box, especially in that only good followers were used in the experiment. Some of the ducklings – the experimental group – were given an electric shock in the runway on the seventh, eighth, ninth and tenth days, before being confronted in the same runway with the familiar moving box. Thus each experimental duckling was conditioned to fear the runway. The result was that the experimental subjects followed the box better than the control subjects which had not learned to associate the runway with pain or discomfort. Thus, while other interpretations cannot necessarily be excluded, it would appear likely that fear of the environment drove the experimental animals towards the familiar figure.

Earlier, Moltz and Rosenblum (1958b), using Peking ducklings, carried out an experiment of a rather different kind. They placed ducklings individually for one hour in the runway before confronting them in the same runway with a moving box. The experimental birds were found to be less good at following the box than the control birds which had not been previously accustomed to the runway. It is likely that the control animals, being strange to the runway at the time of the test, feared the runway more than the habituated experimental animals. In consequence the control animals may have been driven more strongly towards the figure than the experimental animals, and thus followed the box more closely and vigorously.

A rather decisive experiment would consist of training individually two groups of animals in a runway, and then testing individually one group with the familiar figure in the familiar runway, and the other group with the same figure in an unfamiliar runway. Given enough experience, the subjects in the latter group could be expected to follow better than the subjects tested in the home runway, provided the tests were sufficiently sensitive. This better performance would have been due to the 'trauma' associated with the removal to the new runway. The alternative to this procedure would be to test all the animals in the same home runway, but alter the features of the runway for some subjects and not for others. Such an alteration could consist simply of an addition of some stationary objects to the runway, of altering the colour of the walls, and so on. The conditions of the test would be much like those that restored the following of 'satiated' chicks (see Chapter 5).

Strangeness is not, of course, the sole basis of fear. Fear may be aroused in any individual by very intense stimuli as well as by insufficiency of stimulation (Hebb, 1946). Examples of the former are loud noises, dazzlingly bright lights, and the like; examples of sensory deficit would be darkness, prolonged solitude and so on. Otherwise, however, early fears are fears of the strange. It has been repeatedly demonstrated that novel stimuli are liable to invoke fear (see, for example: Hebb, 1946; Melzack, 1952; Montgomery, 1955; Thompson and Melzack, 1956; and more recently in the field of imprinting: Moltz and Stettner, 1961; Salzen, 1962).

Melzack (1952) reviewed previous studies by several investigators of fear responses to strange objects in chimpanzees. He himself studied fear of stationary and moving objects in twenty-six dogs. Melzack found that harmless strange moving objects tended to evoke fear more readily than similar stationary objects. He concluded that some experience, or learning 'other than conditioning' was a prerequisite of avoidance responses. Thompson and Melzack (1956) later expressed the view (1) that fear could be evoked by 'the unusual or the unexpected', and (2) that such fear could not be a result of conditioning.

Menzel (1963) quotes earlier studies indicating that infant chimpanzees may show fear as soon as they are capable of discriminating an object as novel. As Salzen (1963a) puts it, 'fear . . . develops with experience rather than with age'. Thus it takes chicks two or three days before they can recognise any figure as new. Infant rhesus monkeys take much longer; they begin to develop fear responses to strange stimuli at twenty to forty days after birth (Harlow, 1961), and show fear of strange objects at forty to fifty days (Harlow and Zimmermann, 1959).

### (iii) Fear and imprinting

To ask at what age fear first makes its appearance is to ask the wrong question. If distress calls alone are taken as an indication of fear, then in domestic chicks fear might be said to be in evidence at any time from hatching onwards (Salzen, 1962). If, however, flight is taken as the criterion of fear, then fear responses in chicks may become pronounced at around twenty-four hours. But, as we have seen, the onset of fear cannot be said to depend on age as such; it is greatly influenced by the nature of the animal's very early experiences.

A strongly imprinted animal will approach in a choice situation a familiar figure, and this in itself entails some movement away from things unfamiliar. This movement-away thus appears to be a consequence of imprinting. Hinde (1961), however, suggests that the 'tendency to flee from strange objects usually matures rather later than the tendency to follow or beg from them'. But recognition of strangeness requires experience. Whether maturation is or is not an important factor in the development of fearfulness, the tendency to flee from strange objects must be acquired in so far as 'knowledge' of what is strange is acquired.

We have seen that chicks imprinted to one another increasingly show fear of unfamiliar moving objects, and cannot be readily imprinted to them after the age of three to four days. Salzen (1962) reported that newly hatched chicks needed about twenty-four hours of some kind of imprinting before new objects could be sufficiently strange to them to be 'actively' feared. Earlier, Ramsay and Hess (1954) reported that ducklings, too, showed no appreciable fear during the first twenty-four hours of life.

But fear of a figure does not necessarily prevent the animal from eventually becoming imprinted to it. The fear may gradually be so completely overcome that approach, following, and imprinting are possible. Many investigators have observed cases of young birds at first avoiding a moving figure and later following it (Fabricius 1951a, Jaynes 1957, Weidmann 1958, Guiton 1959, Sluckin and Salzen 1961). However, according to Hess (1959a) birds that are induced to follow objects in this way do not, in fact, become imprinted to these objects. It should not prove difficult to put this suggestion to an experimental test.

The view advanced by Sluckin and Salzen (1961), Salzen (1962) and Sluckin (1962) that imprintability ends as a result of imprinting, or that fear develops with imprinting rather than independently of imprinting, was adumbrated as far back as 1950 by Alley and Boyd. These investigators found that young coots were fully imprinted to their parents at twenty-four hours of age; from then on they showed fear of human beings, and imitative calls and feeding by people did not allay their fear. Furthermore, four-day old coots that had not been imprinted to their parents were found to be indifferent to them, or even fear them, despite the fact that the adult birds showed strong parental behaviour in response to the sight of the young ones.

A form of fear reaction in precocial birds that has received relatively little attention is immobility. Salzen (1963a) distinguished between freezing in a normal position, and the immobility response of the animal to being handled and turned on its side or its back. Ratner and Thompson (1960) found that immobility reactions did not occur in domestic chicks until seven to ten days after hatching. Prior handling was found to shorten significantly the duration of immobility on test, when the bird was turned on its side. It appeared that the unfamiliarity of the experience which evoked immobility could be reduced by prior testing and handling; the result of this was a reduction in the fear responses to being turned, indicated by a shorter duration of the immobility response.

Salzen (1963a), too, reported that immobility was absent in domestic chicks before the seventh day after hatching. He found that the immobility responses of socially reared chicks lasted longer than those of chicks reared in isolation. Whenever a socially raised chick was held down on its back in the sight of other chicks, its immobility tended to last less long. Salzen suggested that the separation of a chick from its companions to which it had been imprinted enhanced its fear of the new experience and, hence, lengthened its immobility. The presence of the chick's companions during an immobility test reduced the novelty of the situation, thereby reducing the intensity of fear, and hence the duration of immobility.

### (iv) Imprinting, anxiety and primary drives

Fear, in the ordinary sense, is fear of something or someone; when we talk of fear, we imply that there is an object of rear. Anxiety, on the other hand, may be said to be a general, object-free condition of fearfulness. Some learning theorists make no distinction between fear and anxiety (see Mowrer, 1939), though others recognise differences (e.g. Miller, 1948, 1951). Learning theory lays particular stress on the acquirability of anxiety. Mowrer (1939) considered anxiety to be 'the conditioned form of pain reaction', an acquired secondary drive; and this view has gained wide currency.

It is debatable whether manifestations of anxiety, as well as those of fear, are observable in association with imprinting. What are considered to be indications of anxiety – distress calls, frequent startle responses, frequent defecation – are not easily separable from indications of fear; although the main index of fear, at least in imprinting studies, is flight from particular objects and situations.

Moltz (1960) considered that a newly hatched bird showed little anxiety; for although it might make distress calls, it displayed little general restlessness. Now moving objects readily catch the young bird's attention. And so Moltz put forward the suggestion that the association of the state of low anxiety with an attention-evoking object led to the acquisition by the object of 'the capacity to elicit certain anatomically controlled components of the drive state'. Such a proposition, and the language in which it is couched, may appear to ethologists and a good many psychologists outside America to be somewhat strange. The proposition and its language are, however, very much in keeping with the drive-cum-learning-theory tradition.

An early type of learning theory was advanced by the founder of behaviourism, J. B. Watson. Using Pavlov's conditioning situation as a paradigm, Watson contended in the early-twenties that learning consisted of associations of stimuli and responses which resulted from repeated contiguity in time of such pairs. However, it soon became clear that a mere repetition of temporal contiguity did not necessarily lead to the development of associations. Then in the thirties C. L. Hull constructed a theory in which the so-called Law of Effect, first put forward at the turn of the century by E. L. Thorndike, became, in a new guise, the mainspring of all learning. According to this view, which soon became quite widely accepted, a response was learned only when it was rewarded – in other words, when it was followed by a consummatory act, such as eating, drinking, or mating, or an escape from a painful situation. Thus, the primary drives for learning were thought to be rooted in physiological disequilibria, or bodily needs. And drive reduction, considered to be essential for learning to occur, was thought to be associated with the restoration of homeostasis. But some drives could also be acquired or learned, and these secondary drives could themselves then provide the motive power for learning (see, for example, Miller, 1951).

Undoubtedly, much learning is reward-learning. But a good deal of learning results from punishment. In this type of learning situation punishment is incurred for wrong responses while correct moves are not rewarded. This is known as avoidance-learning. Avoidance-learning cannot be easily explained in terms of the Law of Effect, because incorrect responses are *not repeatedly* stamped out; being avoided, they are just not made. To make avoidance-learning fit into a general theory built upon the Law of Effect, Mowrer and others developed a subsidiary theory of anxiety-learning. Anxiety was said to result from avoidance conditioning, i.e. learning to respond to a situation in such a way as to avoid punishment (avoid the negative reinforcing stimulus). Anxiety having been acquired, much subsequent learning was considered to be tied up with anxiety reduction (see fuller discussion in, for example, Bindra, 1959, or Broadbent, 1961).

As we have seen, according to Moltz (1960), the newly hatched bird is at the start in a state of low anxiety, largely characterised by the absence of any varied, restless activity. This state becomes associated with a moving object; that is, the animal learns that the moving object stands for the rewarding state of low anxiety. As a result of such conditioning 'the object acquires the capacity to function as a reinforcer, henceforth mediating new learning'. Subsequently those responses that are instrumental in bringing the animal closer to the familiar object are rewarded with consequential anxiety-reduction; therefore, following and imprinting take place. As we shall see later, such an explanation of imprinting is not the most parsimonious, or indeed necessary; but it is likely to appeal to those theorists who are convinced that all learning must be reinforced or associated with drive-reduction. It is interesting to note that Moltz (1963) himself has expressed doubt about his earlier view, which – he says – regarded imprinting as 'essentially a classical-instrumental conditioning sequence centering on the arousal and reduction of emotionality'.

As we saw at the end of the last chapter, the critical period for imprinting, according to Moltz (1960), lasts only as long as does the state of low anxiety. This is said to occur normally during a brief period early in the animals' life. But imprinting could also occur at other times, in fact, whenever low anxiety is associated with any dominant new stimulation. On the other hand a chick that is cold, and therefore presumably, in some sense, in a state of anxiety, could be expected, as pointed out by Salzen and Tomlin (1963), not be susceptible to imprinting. However, these investigators found that this was not the case. They remarked in conclusion that 'the sight of the moving object *produces* the "low anxiety" state rather than becomes associated with it'. The initial fearlessness of an animal may be regarded as being simply due to the fact that imprinting, which requires time, has not yet taken place. However, why should the relative absence of fear be sufficient to initiate imprinting? In other words, how are the initial approach and following responses motivated?

We saw in Chapter 3 that initial approach and following responses could be regarded as arising from primary rather than from derived behaviour tendencies. The view that early filial responses are unconditioned is at variance with the rather widely held theoretical position according to which all primary tendencies displayed by living organisms have to do with their biological needs for the requisite food, temperature, etc. On this view, physiological needs plus learning can account for all motives. Not arising from narrowly physiological needs, approach and following must accordingly be learned. And the concept of anxiety had to be introduced in connection with imprinting as a first step towards explaining how these early filial responses might be learned.

Although early approach and following do not appear to satisfy any 'primary' visceral needs, there is no evidence whatsoever that they are learned. Therefore the conclusion must be that these tendencies are primary in a broader sense, but are not 'biogenically' based. The early filial responses could be likened to the tendency to seek sweet-tasting substances. Both are biologically useful, but neither leads invariably to the satisfaction of any biogenic needs. Just as sweet substances have usually but not always some food value, so also approach and following usually but not always lead to the safety provided by parent-animals.

There is now an accumulation of observational and experimental evidence indicating that exploratory and manipulatory tendencies, though not physiologically rewarding, are primary rather than derived (cf., Harlow, 1953a, Barnett, 1958, Glanzer, 1958; see also Chapter 9, Section (iii)). Likewise, there appears to be in certain neonate animals an inherent drive to approach and follow certain sources of stimulation. And in the absence of any evidence that this disposition is acquired, there is no need to regard it as other than innate. Furthermore, we shall see in Chapter 9 that imprinting, as distinct from initial filial responses, cannot be readily fitted into the framework of existing learning theory. Perhaps the time is ripe for new theoretical formulations concerning both basic motives and learning.

# Chapter 8

# EARLY AND LATER LEARNING

Imprinting occurs characteristically, if not exclusively, in the young. In as far as it occurs in the young, imprinting is a form of early learning; although much or most of early learning is not imprinting at all. It has been the hope of many theorists that it would one day be possible to demonstrate that all learning is essentially of one kind, that is, that learning in all circumstances depends upon only one type of mechanism. Some learning theorists have come to think that there must be more than one kind of learning. However, perhaps the more prevalent view tends to be that there are as yet 'no necessary or sufficient reasons for deciding that there is more than one kind' of learning (Bugelski, 1956), even though, quite clearly, different *kinds of behavior* are learned.

This theoretical problem has been to some extent by-passed in the layout of most of the books concerned with learning. Text-books generally group under separate headings the various kinds of learned behaviour and learning procedures; thus, the topics dealt with would be, for instance, classical conditioning, instrumental learning, the transfer of training, and so forth. Such, then, are the distinctions commonly made between one and another sort of learning.

However, the distinction between learning in infancy (and perhaps adolescence), i.e. early learning, and learning in adult life, i.e. later learning, largely cuts across the usual classifications. Now, much attention has been given by Hebb (1949) to some differences between early and later learning. Other contrasting features between early and later learning have been considered more recently by Thorpe (1961) and by Vince (1961).

It would appear that the distinction between early and later learning may in one way be conceived of as essentially temporal: in the life of every individual early learning is succeeded by later learning; and, as early learning leaves behind some traces, so it may be expected that the process of later learning will be in some measure affected by these traces. But secondly, it may be supposed that, since some neuro-physiological changes occur in the individual as he matures and grows older, the very mechanism of learning could undergo certain changes with age.

The first of these two propositions is concerned partly with transfer effects. The implication is that it could be demonstrated that early learning is – as Clarke puts it* – foundational. Certainly some of the studies of imprinting have indicated that attachments established at the start of the animal's life may be remarkably durable and important in shaping the animal's later behaviour. However, our knowledge to date of the impact that this kind of early training may have is meagre. Numerous and diverse longitudinal studies of imprinted individuals are needed to augment our knowledge of the lasting effects of early imprinting.

The other proposition is concerned with the differences between early and later learning in the very nature of the process. The neuro-logical facts concerning brain development are suggestive. Thus, in human beings, during the first two years of life outgrowths of cortical cell dendrites (known as spikes or gemmuli) continue to develop, and consequently nerve-cell inter-connections also continue to develop (Russell, 1959). Russell suggested that human learning could be particularly important during those two first years of life when the brain is still in the developing and relatively malleable stage. It might also be suggested that learning during the two early years is unimportant since it occurs when the brain is not yet fully developed and perhaps not capable of proper functioning. At any rate, in view of the anatomical differences between the brains of the very young and the not so young individuals, it seems not unlikely that the very young differ from the not so young in the way they learn.

Before considering any possible differences in the mode of learning we may ask whether some widely-studied, simple learning processes can occur both in the course of early learning and later learning. The evidence in this respect is equivocal. Earlier failures to condition very young animals have been more recently attributed to the lack of suitable conditions for learning in the previous studies rather than to

* Professor A. D. B. Clarke – in Symposium on Early Learning at the Annual Conference of the British Psychological Society, Bristol, 1962.

any general insusceptibility of the very young to conditioning. Nevertheless, human infants appear to be far less readily conditioned by Pavlovian methods than older children; Kantrow (1937) reviewed early studies, and these had indicated that classical conditioning was either impossible or difficult to attain in the youngest infants. Susceptibility to conditioning in children appears, broadly speaking, to improve with age; see review by Munn, 1954.

Scott and Marston (1950) and Scott (1958b) indicated that neonatal puppies could hardly be conditioned. But Stanley, Cornwell, Poggiani and Trattner (1963) reported food-reinforced instrumental conditioning in puppies only one day old; they also mentioned other studies of dogs which indicated that stable aversive conditioning, which is impossible to achieve at the start of life, could be established at about two weeks of age. Stone (1929a,b) extensively investigated the learning abilities of rats at various ages; he found no consistent pattern and concluded that such age differences as were found in learning were due to motivational differences. Biel (1940), however, who studied rats from sixteen to twenty-nine days old found that their ability to learn a multiple-T water maze improved with age; see also Munn, 1950.

Very little is as yet known about the conditionability of the young animals which are frequently used in imprinting studies. James and Binks (1963) found that domestic chicks did not learn to escape or to avoid electric shock on the day of hatching. The day after hatching, chicks did learn to escape from shock, but did not learn to avoid it. However, on the third day of life some chicks could be also conditioned to avoid shock; and on the fifth day after hatching the majority of the experimental chicks were avoidance-trained.

A fresh approach to the understanding of age differences in learning is due to Vince, who has extensively studied instrumental learning in passerine birds. In one investigation adolescent and mature chaffinches, greenfinches and canaries were given the task of pulling up a string to obtain food suspended on it (Vince, 1958). Comparisons between the younger and older birds in terms of an overall ability to learn were inconclusive; however, comparisons in terms of different aspects of learning efficiency were much more rewarding. Two aspects of behaviour were considered: (1) the ability to learn to respond appropriately to the situation, and (2) the ability to learn to stop responding in the absence of reinforcement. The younger birds were found to be more efficient at learning to respond to the demands of the situation; the younger birds were generally more active and responsive, and consequently tended to hit sooner upon the correct solution of the problem. On the other hand, the ability to learn not to respond to inappropriate simuli was found to be better established in adult birds.

In another investigation Vince (1959) applied the same kind of analysis to the learning of different tasks by canaries and green-finches. In this study, the birds had to learn to discriminate between a dish containing food and covered with a white lid and an empty dish covered with a black lid. The mastery of this task consisted of learning not to respond to the wrong lid; thus, the task mainly called for the exercise of the ability to inhibit the tendency to continue responding to the full range of stimuli. The results of this investigation were some-what uncertain; none-the-less learning in adults was found to be rather more efficient than learning in adolescents.

The abilities to learn to respond and to learn not to respond depend not solely on age, but also on the earlier experiences of the animals (see Vince, 1961). However, maturation appears to be a very important factor. Indeed, Vince (1960) showed that the responsiveness of the great tit, as indicated by the time spent pulling about and pecking a small, brightly coloured object, rises rapidly to a maximal level at about thirteen weeks of age, that is, relatively early in life. On the other hand, the capacity of this bird not to respond uselessly reaches its peak considerably later, at about thirty-five weeks of age. In Vince's view learning ability in general is too crude a concept for develop-mental psychology; different features of learning ability merit their own investigations.

Earlier studies of the differential growth of learning abilities, some carried out in the early decades of this century, have been surveyed by Vince (1961). Studies of the rat, in particular, suggest that the young are the quicker learners whenever activity as such helps; for activity is strongly associated with ability to form new responses. In contrast, whenever ability to control and direct activity is important in the learning task, older animals tend to be the more efficient. It has been known for a long time (see, for instance, Luria, 1932) that children are, on the whole, as responsive to stimulation as adults, if not more so; but they have greater difficulty in inhibiting, controlling and direct-ing their responses.

Evidence is accumulating to indicate a variety of differences, some slight and some considerable, between early learning and later learning. Hebb (1949) thought that early reward/punishment learning was, on the whole, very slow. The implication of Vince's studies is that, slow or otherwise, early learning is associated with varied and intense responsiveness. This condition of the animal is also a prerequisite of imprinting; for imprinting cannot occur unless exposure to stimulation makes an impact on the individual.

The effectiveness of the impact of stimulation, as far as responsiveness is concerned, would appear to depend on both the age and the previous sensory experience of the individual. For sensory deprivation at an early age could (1) arrest perceptual development, and (2) both arrest it and bring about superimposed atrophic processes (Riesen, 1961). If imprinting is to result from initial responses, inhibitory powers must develop, so that positive responses to new stimulus configurations may be suppressed. This ability, too, appears to depend on both the age and the previous experience of the individual. For, while powers of inhibition mature, they also depend on the accumulation of sufficient experience to make possible the discrimination between the familiar and the strange.

# Chapter 9

# LEARNING BY REINFORCEMENT
# AND EXPOSURE

The notions of learning theory held by psychologists and by physiologists are disparate rather than conflicting. Physiologists theorise about the neural mechanisms involved in learning, whereas psychologists, *qua* psychologists, tend to be concerned with unifying principles of learning. These unifying principles may or may not be couched in physiological terms; but such traditional postulates as the principle of association or the principle of reinforcement are not. A number of psychological theories of learning have been put forward this century, but no single all-embracing theory has gained general acceptance. Likewise, a number of views are at present current as to how imprinting is related to learning in general. These differing views, not always explicitly stated, may be found, among some others, in papers by Hess (1959a, 1959c), Hinde (1961), James (1960c), Moltz (1960, 1963), Salzen (1962), and Sluckin (1962).

Learning is a very broad term. It could be said to refer to relatively lasting changes in behaviour resulting from practice. The word, practice, is used to exclude changes dependent on maturation and aging; and by referring to the enduring character of the behavioural changes, we set aside those changes that are associated with fatigue, adaptation and the like. Even so, practice does not invariably lead to learning; and some learning does not readily show itself as a change in overt behaviour. Conditioning is a distinctly narrower term than learning. It may be said to refer merely to certain training procedures. Now imprinting is, or course, a form of learning. The question before us is whether imprinting may be regarded as a form of conditioning.

Quite early, Fabricius (1951a) expressed the view that 'it is not possible to draw a sharp line between imprinting and ordinary conditioning'. Hinde (1955a) inclined to the view 'that imprinting is not fundamentally different from other forms of learning'. Klopfer (1961) expressed the opinion that only the critical period could be said to distinguish imprinting from other forms of learning, and suggested that 'intermediate processes link imprinting to conventional types of learning'; see also Gottlieb (1963b). Moltz (1961a) agreed with Klopfer that the critical period was a unique characteristic of imprinting; and as we have seen earlier, Moltz (1960) initially attempted to show that imprinting was a form of classical-cum-instrumental conditioning. Lorenz (1955) himself thought that 'typical imprinting tapers off into learning', and he ventured the view that 'imprinting is definitely one type of conditioning'.

### (i) Association and reinforcement

Conditioning involves the building up of associations between stimuli and responses. The view that associations of some kind underlie learning is very much older than the studies of conditioning. This view is so prevalent as to be acceptable almost without being questioned. A widely used general text-book of psychology states that 'One factor that is common to all situations in which learning takes place is *association*' (Morgan, 1961). Be this as it may, Hess (1959a) denied that 'imprinting is identical with simple association learning', and later (Hess, 1962b) deprecated attempts 'to fit the imprinting phenomenon into the association learning framework'. It is somewhat uncertain what Hess means by 'simple association learning', but it is implicit in Hess's remarks that, in his view, it would be misguided to regard imprinting as a form of conditioning. Now, it is difficult to maintain that association in some sense is absent from learning of any kind, including imprinting. But it is entirely defensible to argue that conditioning is characteristically associative in a way that imprinting is not.

In conditioning the pairing of stimuli and responses is selective: either one out of a range of possible stimuli becomes associated with a given response, or one particular response out of a repertoire of possible responses becomes associated with some stimulus. Thus an associative link is established between certain stimuli and certain responses, which have not been initially associated together.

Many learning theorists assert that whilst association by contiguity is a necessary condition for learning it is not a sufficient one. A lasting association is built up through reinforcement. Reinforcement, in the form of reward or punishment, is readily identified in any form of conditioning. Without continued reinforcement a conditioned association is subject to extinction.

Imprinting generally starts with 'built-in', unconditioned approach responses to the source of stimuli of a wide variety. The given stimulus configuration continues to elicit filial responses, but after a time, any novel stimuli begin to be ignored and, later, feared. There is no selective pairing of stimuli and responses, as in conditioning. In imprinting, the initial bond between stimuli and responses continues to be strengthened and to become exclusive. It is a semantic consideration whether this consolidation may or may not reasonably be called association. If the phrase, associative learning, is to refer to learning in which associations are built up only through conditioning, then imprinting is a form of *non-associative learning*.

In conditioning, the reinforcing stimulus is necessary for the building up of the bond between the conditioned stimulus and the conditioned response; but the reinforcing stimulus itself is separate from, or external to, the pair which are becoming associated. Primary reinforcing agents in conventional conditioning are conditions that meet the basic physiological needs of the organism and restore its physiological homeostasis. In imprinting there is no external reinforcement. The development of an attachment to the stimulus figure does not depend on a physiological reward, such as food, water, warmth, etc. The releasing stimulus itself is attractive from the start, and becomes more attractive as the organism continues to be exposed to it. In this sense such a stimulus could be regarded as reward. Therefore, although it does not depend on external reinforcement, imprinting may be said to be a self-reinforcing process. Hinde, Thorpe and Vince (1956) referred to imprinting as self-reinforced learning. However, in so far as the term, reinforcement, implies or suggests external reinforcement, imprinting may equally, if not preferably, be described as a form of *non-reinforced learning*.

It is not perhaps very important to decide what labels to attach or not to attach to imprinting. What matters is precisely *how* imprinting compares with other forms of learning. Now, from the outset, laboratory studies have shown that the several features of imprinting, which originally seemed unique, do not, in fact, set aside imprinting from other learning processes. Thus, as we have seen earlier, imprinting is not instantaneous, and when it is very rapid, it is still incremental like other types of learning. Nor has imprinting been found to be in any sense irreversible: imprinting generalises to a range of stimuli, and

8

imprinted attachments, including sexual ones, are not exclusive. The sensitive period for imprinting is often not at all sharply defined; and, in any case, there are also relatively sensitive periods for forms of learning other than imprinting. All these findings seemed to suggest that imprinting is not a special form of learning (e.g. Hinde, 1955a; Hinde, 1962b). And, as we have seen, some investigators have thought of imprinting as conditioning; but, clearly, imprinting is neither associative nor reinforced, at least, not in the same way as conditioning, whether classical or instrumental.

It has long been recognised as somewhat debatable whether it is advisable to use the one term, conditioning, in reference to the two types of sequence of events, classical conditioning and instrumental conditioning. However, classical and instrumental conditioning have many features in common. So much so that classical and instrumental conditioning are generally regarded as two different forms of essentially the same process (Hilgard and Marquis, 1961), although some learning theorists (e.g., Mowrer, 1960) put more stress on the differences between them than on the similarities. Let us consider a little more closely certain features of both kinds of conditioning *vis-à-vis* imprinting.

In conditioning, two stimulus patterns are necessarily involved: the unconditioned stimulus (UCS) and the conditioned stimulus (CS). As a result of learning the animal or human being eventually acts in some way in response to the CS. The UCS is the reinforcer: its continued presence increases the probability of the conditioned act occurring whenever the CS is presented. Thus the conditioned stimulus becomes in the course of learning the signal which sets off the particular response. In imprinting one stimulus only is involved, the stimulus which elicits the approach/following response. This stimulus serves both as the signal and as the reinforcer, in that it not only sets off the approach/following behaviour but also increases the probability of this behaviour being elicited by the stimulus on subsequent occasions.

Like conditioning, imprinting brings about changes in behaviour; and as in conditioning, such changes show themselves in altered probabilities of some behavioural events – in increases in the speed of responding, in increases in the magnitude of responses, and so on. In conditioning, the removal of reinforcement brings about a gradual extinction of the conditioned responses. In imprinting the situation is rather different, partly because the conditional and reinforcing stimuli are not separate. As noted in earlier chapters, the removal of the stimulus in imprinting does not necessarily start a gradual extinction of the imprinted attachment.

According to Hess (1959a, 1959c, 1962b) primacy of experience is of fundamental importance in imprinting, in contrast with association learning; in other words, early imprinting is said to be better retained than later imprinting, whereas in association learning retention depends more on recency than primacy. Furthermore, according to Hess, not only does imprinting require no separate reinforcement, but it is actually improved by punishment. As Hinde (1962b) points out, the view that primacy is more important in imprinting than recency cannot be readily substantiated or tested. A young animal imprinted to one figure is less easily imprinted to a second figure. There is little reason to suppose that, even if the degrees of learning of the two figures could be equalised, the attachment to the first figure would be more strongly retained than the attachment to the second figure.

Again, as mentioned by Hinde, Hess offers no evidence to support his contention that punishment enhances imprinting. More recently, Kovach and Hess (1963) set out to investigate this in chicks. They trained their subjects for fifteen minutes in a circular runway; experimental subjects were shocked through electrodes attached to their wings, while controls were not shocked. The findings were equivocal. The chicks' following was tested at eighteen hours, thirty-two hours and forty-eight hours. At the earliest age shocks helped following, but at the two later ages following was found to have been hindered by the shocks. Punishment is, in fact, an entirely extraneous factor in imprinting, whereas it is an integral factor of escape and avoidance conditioning.

In so far as the stimulus figure may be said to constitute a reward in imprinting, reward, unlike punishment, is an integral factor of imprinting. The removal of the stimulus figure has different effects in different circumstances. The short-term effect is to strengthen, rather than weaken, the outward signs of the animal's attachment to the stimulus. It will be remembered that Sluckin and Taylor (1964) found that chicks imprinted to a moving object discriminated between it and a new moving object significantly better after an interval of some minutes than immediately after training. When the discrimination test is given after a much longer interval, then retention is less. Much as in conditioning, motivational factors and the rôle of transfer in the performance must be taken into account in assessing how much has been learned and retained in imprinting. Low retention score immediately after training can be due to a low motivational state, or drive satiation; and poor performance on test, when training and test situations differ in regard to the movement of the imprinting object, could be due to low positive transfer, or poor generalisation of responses to stimuli with different attributes (Sluckin and Taylor, 1964).

In conditioning, the response to the CS generalises to a varying extent to other stimuli. This spreading of responses to a range of stimuli follows the so-called generalisation gradient away from the CS. Whenever responses to one stimulus are repeatedly reinforced while responses to a somewhat similar stimulus are not reinforced, discriminatory responses gradually develop between the two stimuli. In the early stages of the imprinting process the animal spreads its responses to stimuli relatively similar to the original stimulus configuration. However, as the subject continues to be exposed to a particular figure, it gradually acquires the ability to discriminate between it and all strange stimuli. This learning appears to be purely a function of the time of exposure to any given stimulus pattern (Sluckin and Salzen, 1961). Thus, the longer the young animal experiences any stimulus configuration, the more sharply it later discriminates in favour of the familiar figure and against all others.

It is yet to be established to what extent this way of learning to differentiate among stimuli also obtains in conditioning. It is known that generalisation tends to vary inversely with the animal's experience of the given CS coupled with UCS. It has been suggested by Rheingold that this may be the case in mature individuals as a result of some form of pre-learning familiarisation with the environment (Foss, 1961). It is perhaps possible that a diminution of generalisation after continued conditioning is due to an element of hitherto undetected imprinting-like learning coupled with the conditioning process.

### (ii) Interaction of imprinting and conditioning

One form of interaction between imprinting-like behaviour and conditioning was investigated by James (1959). Having first found that very young domestic chicks tended to approach a source of intermittent light, James set out to see if this light could be used as an unconditioned reinforcing stimulus in standard classical conditioning procedures. He used as his subjects two-day-old chicks; the conditioned stimulus was a turquoise polythene ball suspended near the flickering light. Each chick was exposed to the ball and flickering light for five minutes at a time, altogether ten times. These sessions were spread over five days, and on the sixth day the chick was tested with the ball but without the flickering light. James found that his experimental chicks approached the ball when presented alone, and followed it when it was moved up and down the runway. His control chicks, which had previous experience of the ball without the flickering light, were tested in the same way as the experimental subjects; they were found to be attracted by the ball significantly less than the former. Thus James showed that conditioning could be superimposed, as it were, upon imprinting, or at least, upon filial responses.

Further experiments using a flickering light source as UCS and stationary 'lures' as CS were performed by James (1960a), and by Abercrombie and James (1961). In the latter study, chicks were first exposed to a flickering light paired with a stationary object. From the third day on some chicks were tried repeatedly with the stationary object only. In the language of conditioning studies, this was an attempt to establish experimental extinction. The trials, however, did not bring about any decrement in the responses to the CS. It thus looked as if stationary objects could become attractive in their own right. Conditioning was perhaps merely helping to speed up the establishment of the 'approach fixation'.

However, Abercombie and James (1961) drew attention to the finding that 'learning in adult mammals is particularly resistant to extinction if competing responses are not available during the extinction trials'. In the actual experiment the chicks had little opportunity to acquire in the course of training any responses other than approach fixation. The investigators did not regard the persistence of the conditioned response as having been due to the special nature of the UCS, the flicker. On the contrary, they reported that a conditioned approach response based on food reinforcement was also resistant to extinction when there were no competing responses during the extinction sessions.

Like James, Klopfer (1959b) noted classical conditioning in association with imprinting. He found that some of his experimental sheldrakes learned to respond positively to certain sounds which had been previously linked with a visual model to which these birds had been imprinted. Thus, Klopfer used the sight of a moving object as the UCS; this served as the reinforcing agent, enabling a conditioned response to particular sound signals to be established. It is possible, however, that in suitable conditions the sound signals alone would have been sufficient to evoke approach fixation.

An attempt to use the following response of chicks as a reward in instrumental conditioning was made by Campbell and Pickleman (1961). Domestic chicks were first individually imprinted to a cardboard cube. Subsequently a T-maze conditioning situation was set up in which the goal was the imprinting runway with the object out of sight. The chicks were given fifty 'lessons' spread over ten days. They learned to take the correct turning in a typically instrumental fashion; that is, the learning curves for the chicks showed gradual increases in the proportion of correct responses and in the speed of running to the goal. Control chicks spent as much time individually in an empty runway, otherwise similar to the experimental one. The empty runway was then used as the goal in T-maze conditioning trials. However, in this case, the chicks did not learn the maze at all. It is clear that the imprinting situation can be successfully used as the UCS when imprinted subjects are instrumentally conditioned. An interesting feature of the Campbell/Pickleman study was the finding that learning the maze was not dependent on a steady series of consummatory acts of following. The acquired behaviour of taking the correct turn continued to be more and more efficiently performed as training went on; the actual time spent at following the object at the goal decreased with training. There is no reason to suppose that attachment to the object diminished with instrumental learning. Only the manifestations of the attachment diminished, possibly as a result of 'drive satiation' (cf. Sluckin and Taylor, 1964).

A promising field of research is one of interaction between conditioning and imprinting within the conditioning situation. It is, for instance, possible that instrumental reward conditioning is in some circumstances affected by imprinting which goes on at the same time. Thus, as the young animal learns to associate a given stimulus pattern with a reward, it spends increasingly more time with this particular stimulus pattern. As a result, in addition to becoming conditioned, it may also become imprinted to it. Such imprinting could be a factor in speeding up and strengthening the formation of the stimulus-response bonds. Further research may show in what circumstances this could occur.

### (iii) Exposure learning

An imprinted attachment to a figure can be formed only when the organism has acquired the power to recognise the figure, i.e. to differentiate between it and anything else. This ability is a necessary condition for imprinting, but not a sufficient one. The learning of the characteristics of the environment need not, of course, entail the formation of any attachments; the subject's familiarity with the environment can manifest itself in other ways.

Sluckin and Salzen (1961) expressed the view that the discrimination between the familiar and the strange, consequent upon imprinting, is acquired not by conditioning but through perceptual learning; Sluckin (1962) later attempted to develop this suggestion. It should be noted that the phrase, perceptual learning, is somewhat ambiguous; it has been used in psychological literature in a number of different ways. Gibson and Gibson (1955) pointed out that perceptual learning might refer mainly to (1) the influence of learning on perception, or mainly to (2) the effects of perception in learning. Gibson and Gibson were themselves concerned with the rôle of learning in perception; this section of the present chapter deals, on the other hand, with perception as a basis of learning; that is, we are concerned with learning which is entailed by perceiving, or arises from exposure to stimulation.

This kind of prior learning has been shown to aid rats and other animals in maze running and similar tasks; cf. incidental, or latent learning. Experience of this kind has been found to help animals to solve discrimination problems; see, for example, Siegel (1953), or, Gibson and Walk (1956), Gibson *et al.* (1958) and Walk *et al.* (1959). Lack of such learning has been shown to handicap animals later in coping successfully with environmental exigencies of one kind or another; cf. Bingham and Griffiths (1952), Hymovitch (1952), Forgays and Forgays (1952), Thompson and Heron (1954a,b), Forgus (1954, 1955), Forgays and Read (1962); these studies made it repeatedly clear that the handicapping factor was the lack of perceptual experience rather than any restriction or motor activity.

The ability to apprehend and discriminate is dormant until exposure to stimulation has enabled this ability to develop. In so far as sensory stimulation has any impact at all, it entails perceptual, exposure learning. *Exposure learning* is a telling phrase which has been used for some time by Drever.* It refers unambiguously to the perceptual registration by the organism of the environment to which it is exposed; it thus refers to the familiarisation of the organism with its environment.

* I am greatly indebted to Professor James Drever for suggesting that the phrase 'exposure learning' might be appropriate in this context.

As we have seen in Chapter 5, the evidence is against the view that imprinting depends on the act of following, or the effort expended in following. On the contrary, it looks as if exposure to stimulation, or exposure learning, underlies imprinting. Baer and Gray (1960), having found imprinting to an object to be possible in the absence of any previous following or bodily contact with it, concluded that '*imprinting* is not a learning to follow, but a *learning of the characteristics* of the parent-object'. Perhaps it would have been nearer the truth to say that imprinting depends on the learning of these characteristics, that is, that exposure learning is a prerequisite of the formation of an imprinted attachment.

It looks as though exposure learning is, in a sense, unmotivated, or at least unmotivated by physiological rewards and punishments. It is a semantic issue whether the word, unmotivated, is appropriate in this connection. For it may equally be argued that a living organism has a 'need' to use its sense organs, or a 'drive' to seek stimulation. That is, a living organism is motivated to live, to continue being exposed to stimulation, and thereby to learn. Nissen (1954) argued that:

> The need of organs to function is bodily state which expresses itself in drive behaviour. Capacity is its own motivation. A function or capacity of the sense organs and brain is to perceive and to know, and this is one of the more important drives of all organisms.

Many researches carried out since about 1950 have indicated that the seeking of sensory stimulation must be regarded as a goal of behaviour in its own right. This conclusion emerges from the various animal conditioning studies in which the reward consisted only of sensory stimulation, such as something novel to see or touch. Butler (1953) found that monkeys 'learned a discrimination problem on the basis of visual-exploration incentive'. He established that a wide variety of things to see could be attractive to monkeys (Butler, 1954). Butler concluded that a visual-exploration motive was strong and persistent, and not derived from other drive states.

Harlow, Harlow and Meyer (1950) found that four experimental rhesus monkeys were significantly more efficient at solving a mechanical puzzle after some experience of manipulating it than four control monkeys without the relevant experience. Harlow (1950) reported that two monkeys became better, as time went on, at opening a more complex mechanical puzzle, again without any extraneous incentive. A manipulation drive was postulated, although the contribution of homeostatic drives towards the development of manipulatory behaviour could not be entirely ruled out. Harlow and McClearn (1954) later found that three rhesus monkeys made 'progressive improvement in seven discrimination problems on the basis of manipulation motives'; see discussion by Harlow (1953a, b) of primary drives and motives. Montgomery (1951, 1954) and others have demonstrated that novel stimulation is sought by rats for its own sake, and can act as a reinforcing agent in conditioning; cf. Walk (1960). Miles (1958) found that also in kittens 'manipulatory and exploratory activities are rewarding in their own right'.

The inference that sensory stimulation is a primary need would also appear to emerge from studies of sensory deprivation in human subjects. Bexton, Heron and Scott (1954) formed the judgement that 'the maintenance of normal, intelligent adaptive behaviour requires a continually varied sensory input'. Some supporting evidence for this view comes from the study by Hebb, Heath and Stuart (1954) who found that 'a sudden lowering of normal auditory input' disturbed behaviour which did not, as such 'require auditory acuity for its guidance'. Heron, Doane and Scott (1956) reported visual disturbances after prolonged perceptual isolation.

It looks as though efficiency at coping with the environment is maintained or improved as a result of prior sensory input and exposure learning. We have seen that in the young, variability of behaviour makes for success in instrumental learning (Vince, 1961). It may be that such variability, or exploratory behaviour, is associated with much exposure learning. It could be that exposure learning is particularly important in the young. Normal development includes perhaps much early exposure learning, though later, associative learning substantially takes over. It would appear that exposure learning is at its height when the 'content of mind' is least, at the time when the organism is very young, or is otherwise particularly receptive. The conception of exposure learning is in some ways in keeping with the notion of passive learning which derives from the British empiricist philosophy. For exposure learning appears to depend merely on the impact of sensory stimulation upon the impressionable organism.

### (iv) Imprinting-like behaviour in animals and man
Stimuli of one class that evoke fear are unfamiliar, strange stimuli. But continued exposure to such stimuli tends to allay fear. Hebb (1946) suggested that 'with still further exposure, the formerly strange

object may become not merely tolerated but "liked" and "pleasant"'. This sounds like the onset of imprinting. Such learning occurs most readily in the young or inexperienced. Nevertheless, imprinting-like learning appears also to occur in some circumstances in mature, adult individuals.

Probably the best-attested such occurrence is in she-goats and ewes which become attached to their young soon after parturition. The phenomenon, which had been known for a long time, was investigated systematically by Hersher, Richmond and Moore (1963). These investigators placed sheep and goat dams in a restraining harness at two to twelve hours after parturition, thereby putting each subject in close proximity to an alien young animal, either of its own or of the other species. The females in this way adopted young other than their own within about ten days. Two or three months later all these adoptions were still firmly established. Thus, through forced exposure, any female goat or sheep in an immediate post-natal state of arousal might become attached to any infant lamb or kid.

Scott (1962) wonders whether any animal or person of any age 'exposed to certain individuals or physical surroundings for any length of time, will inevitably become attached to them'. Scott points out that this may account for the strong affection of some neglected children for their cruel parents, or for the peculiar affectional ties that sometimes develop between prisoners and gaolers. This is at present no more than interesting conjecture; speculations like these are reviewed and discussed in Chapter 10.

Also speculative, if rather less so, is our knowledge of the recognition by parent birds of their young. Alley and Boyd (1950) found that parent coots with young under two weeks of age tolerated or even accepted coot-chicks similar in appearance to their own. However, parent coots with older chicks, treated other young, even when similar to their own, as strangers and territorial intruders. The investigators concluded that coots gradually learn to recognise their own young. As they learn to recognise them, they become attached to them. Or, may it be said that parent-coots become imprinted to their young?

We may mention here the supposed learning of the characteristics of their young by parent cichlid fish, which has been cited as evidence for the occurrence of imprinting in fish. This claim appears to have been first made by Baerends and Baerends-van Roon (1950) who stated that adult individuals become imprinted to juveniles (having drawn this conclusion from an earlier study of social behaviour in cichlid fish by Noble and Curtis). Later, Tinbergen (1951) and Thorpe (1956) reiterated this suggestion. More recently, Greenberg (1963a) carried out further experiments and reached the conclusion that care-giving behaviour of parent cichlid fish was governed by 'an internal mechanism regulating the duration of the phases of parental care', and that these fish were 'not imprinted on the species characteristics of their first or subsequent young'. Greenberg (1963b) further stated that 'the reputed ability of cichlid parents to distinguish their own young from those of other species may depend on disparity between the host pair's parental cycle and the stage of development of the foreign young'.

As we saw in Chapter 5, imprinted attachments may develop not only to living or life-like objects but also to a stationary environment. Seemingly before any conclusive evidence of such imprinting in birds was available, Thorpe (1944, 1956) put forward the hypothesis of 'locality imprinting' in insects. Various observations by entomologists of the behaviour of solitary wasps and bees seemed to indicate that imprinting-like attachments by newly emerged organisms might be formed to first-perceived localities. Thorpe also regarded the behaviour of the honey-bee 'as evidence of latent learning and imprinting' in insects.

The restriction of any insect species to a given locality may be due to a variety of ecological factors. There may also be conditioning to certain food plants found in a particular type of environment, rather than to some 'exact locality'. Nevertheless Thorpe believed that 'locality imprinting' might occur in some cases of 'locality restriction'. Thorpe did not, however, class orientation learning by insects as imprinting. This type of learning is exemplified by the locality learning found in the bee-killing digger wasp, *Philanthus*, originally investigated in the nineteen-thirties by Tinbergen; see Tinbergen (1958), Thorpe (1956, 1963).

There is no doubt that each of these wasps learns the details of the environment of its burrow-nest by 'inspecting' the *Gestalt* of the locality. On emerging from its nest each wasp circles over it in widening loops; the wasp then returns to cruise low over the nest before finally flying off to its hunting grounds. Each wasp returns eventually to its own burrow, and does this sometimes more than once a day; it makes a fresh 'survey' of the locality before flying off again. Tinbergen was able to establish that the 'locality studies' made by each wasp were necessary for finding its way back to the nest; and each wasp was found to depend for finding its way back on the topography around its nest remaining essentially unchanged. Thus, when a circle of pine cones, originally around a wasp's nest, was placed some distance away during the wasp's absence, the wasp would on return search for the nest within the cone circle rather than at the original location. This learning is cognitive learning of some kind.* Likewise, perhaps the homing pigeons' knowledge of their home is acquired by topographical locality inspections. However, Thorpe considers these to be associated with reward learning. The pigeon, using the orientation mechanism at its disposal, appears to head for the reward of 'home-comfort' and food. For the present, the rôles of the imprinting and conditioning elements in the acquisition of topographical orientation remain uncertain.

There are forms of learning, clearly akin to imprinting, which have not been in the past interpreted as such. Thus, Scott, Fredericson and Fuller (1951) thought that the lasting effects of early experiences in puppies could be due to very rapid association learning and traumatic experiences. Food rewards, which are known to mould the behaviour of adult mammals, were assumed to underlie the formation of social attachments in the young. Experimental findings soon clouded this view. Scott (1958b) did find that feeding helped socialisation, especially in older puppies. But he expressed some surprise that 'the difference between the hungry and non-hungry animals was not as great as had been expected'. Scott at that time thought that socialisation could only begin in the puppies at the age of about three weeks, because – he believed – puppies were not susceptible to conditioning at an earlier age. Infant animals can be tamed both at the very early and the somewhat later stages in their development. This fact was thought by Hess (1962b) to account for some of the confusion between imprinting and association learning.

In an early study Brodbeck (1954), experimenting with young beagle and cocker spaniel puppies, fed some of them by hand and some by machine; all had contact, however, with human beings. Brodbeck found that the socialisation of puppies did not depend on their being fed by the experimenter. Other investigators were later able to confirm that taming did not primarily depend on reward conditioning, but rather on contact with, or exposure to, people (Scott, 1962). In the

---

* I am grateful to Professor S. G. M. Lee for having drawn my attention to these studies.

light of these findings, as well as others concerning the socialisation of precocial birds through imprinting, and the socialisation of monkeys in the course of development of their affectional responses, Scott (1962) concluded that social tendencies could not be regarded as secondary drives acquired through conditioning; the implication was that social tendencies were acquired, at least in part, through imprinting-like learning.

As indicated in Chapter 2, the formation of attachments by infant monkeys to their mothers, or mother-surrogates, so thoroughly investigated and vividly described by Harlow and his colleagues, appears to be essentially an imprinting-like process.* This process appears to depend on early exposure learning coupled with a development of attachment to the familiar stimulus configurations. Harlow (1961) reports that very early in life rhesus monkeys approach and explore all objects within reach; at some twenty to forty days, however, strange stimulus figures begin to evoke fear responses. Soft body contact is the kind of stimulation provided by the environment which is intrinsically attractive to the baby monkey, just as flicker is attractive to the chick or duckling. Therefore, objects with the 'right' kind of texture elicit approach-and-stay responses, rather than exploratory, approach-and-leave responses. Thereafter, an attachment through familiarity is built up, becoming more exclusive with time. Fear of anything strange 'drives' the baby monkey to the familiar object to which it is attached. The behaviour of a frightened cloth-mother-attached monkey, as described by Harlow (1961), is strikingly similar to that of a frightened moving-box-imprinted chick described by Sluckin and Salzen (1961).

If infant monkeys learn by exposure to stimulation, and become 'imprinted', why not human infants? If human attachments are in any way imprinted, they do not, of course, develop from approach and

* More recently Taylor and Sluckin (1964b) reported a somewhat similar behaviour process in domestic chicks. They initially reared chicks 'in individual pens with a fold of foam-rubber fixed to one of the walls. All the folds looked alike, being covered with smooth plastic surfacing. However, half the folds were also lined with this material while the other half were not and thus remained rough and soft inside. After 36 hours a "wall" of cardboard was lowered in front of the object and then raised again. The responses of the chicks to this test showed the extent of each bird's attachment to the object with which it had been reared. Chicks were found to be more strongly attached to unlined objects than to smooth-lined ones. In a further test responses of chicks were noted to a coloured flag placed in the pen. It was found that the unlined objects tended to be used more often than the others as a shelter and base from which to explore the flag'.

following responses seen in non-altricial birds and mammals. However, human attachments could be initially based on such 'component instinctual responses' as clinging or sucking (Bowlby, 1958). And another component response which could be of importance is smiling (Bowlby, 1957, 1958). Salzen (1963b) found that at first the smiling response appeared to be elicited simply by a 'contrast or change in brightness', rather than by a representation, however crude, of the human face, as reported earlier by Spitz and Wolfe (1946). If further investigations should prove the smiling response to be capable of elicitation by stimuli similar to those that evoke approach and following in young nidifugous birds, then this would substantiate the earlier suggestion of Gray (1958) that smiling and following responses are homologous. It is not as yet clear whether any imprinting-like learning is, in fact, built upon the smiling response.

Chapter 10

# THE LASTING EFFECTS OF EARLY EXPERIENCE

Our knowledge of the long-term effects of imprinting early in life is no more than fragmentary. The paucity of firm findings will have been apparent from our survey of the germane studies in Chapter 4. The lasting effects of imprinting could be treated as part of a wider problem, that of the effects of early exposure learning. It is, however, extremely difficult to separate this type of learning from early learning in general. And the study of the full range of effects of early learning is indeed a vast subject, and, certainly, beyond the scope of this chapter. However, we may take a speculative look at some of the ramifications of imprinting. We shall begin by drawing attention to some boundaries within the field of study of the lasting effects of early experience. Thus we may be able to consider any long-term effects of imprinting against a wider background.

To begin with, a distinction may be made between (1) the lasting effects of early learning in the form of training, and (2) the effects of other kinds of early experience. Of course, any feature of behaviour acquired as a result of any experience may be said in the broadest sense to have been learned. Considering, however, laboratory experiments, we may manifestly distinguish between learning which may be described as resulting from formal training, and learning which is not training in the usual sense. Outside the laboratory, too, such learning as the acquisition of skills and habits falls into the first category; here, later performance is essentially an improved version of earlier performance. Other learning, however, results from the impact of certain experiences upon the subject so that his mode of behaviour undergoes change, but no specific skill or habit is acquired.

Young house pets are trained to be clean indoors, to beg for food, etc.; laboratory rats and mice are taught to run mazes and to press levers; garden birds learn where to find crumbs or bacon rind near the house; in all these cases the animal performs later what it has learned earlier; trained to perform a trick, the subject – even after a long time-interval – will do so when the signal is given. But the value of much early training is that it may be to some degree transferable to new situations. As Hebb (1949) indicated (*Organization of Behaviour, Chapter* 6), later learning may be 'half transfer' from early learning. And, as Harlow (1949) and others, since, have shown, animals are capable of learning how to learn. It appears that such less direct and less obvious effects of early learning may be at least as important as the direct results of training.

Indirect effects of early learning refer to later performance which, although unlike the early performance, is influenced by it. Lack of any training not only often precludes the acquisition of skill and habits; it also affects adversely the subsequent development of general adaptive and learning abilities, as indicated by Hebb (1949), Forgays and Forgays (1952), Thompson and Heron (1954a,b), Forgus (1954, 1955), Thompson and Melzack (1956) and others. Protracted restriction of sensory input in infancy is one special type of early experience which affects later behaviour and personality development. Various environmental factors have been manipulated to discover their long-term effects. These factors may be classified into those associated with (1) constant, long-acting experiences, and (2) brief and relatively intense experiences (cf. Denenberg, 1962; Levine, 1962a,b).

Examples of the former are, prolonged exposure to high and low temperature, bright and dim illumination, the company of other animals and people, and so forth. The latter are exemplified by loud noises of short duration, electric shocks, etc. Our knowledge of the lasting effects of early experiences appeared to Beach and Jaynes (1954) to be equivocal and uncertain; after some years, this is probably still the case. King (1958) furnished a classified survey of the relevant animal-behaviour studies. He noted how these studies had been mainly influenced by the psychoanalytic approach on the one hand, and by Hebb's theory-building on the other.

There have been investigations of considerable interest concerned with the effects of weaning infant rats and puppies at various stages of their development, the effects of the size of the litter in rats, and the effects of the age of separation of young rats and kittens from mother; the aspects of later behaviour considered were learning ability, adaptability, emotionality, and so on. However, it has been rather less difficult to assess the effects of stimulation of short duration, e.g., discontinuous handling and/or discontinuous shocking. While earlier investigators showed that unstimulating environment adversely affected later learning ability, Levine, Chevalier and Korchin (1956) and Levine (1956) reported that, in the case of rats, environment which provided some extra stimulation (even if no more than some momentary experience of being handled every day in infancy) could facilitate the animals' later ability to be conditioned instrumentally. It was found that rats which had been handled and shocked were later not quite so good at such learning as those that had only been handled. Denenberg (1959) reported, however, that shocking infant mice helped subsequent classical conditioning. Denenberg and Bell (1960) showed that mice with some experience of being electrically shocked in infancy were better in certain circumstances at avoidance learning in adulthood. Denenberg and Karas (1960) confirmed the advantageous effects of early handling of rats upon their later learning. It is still an open question as to why such early experiences should lead to a general improvement in adaptability. An element of cognitive exposure learning could be in part responsible.

A great deal has been said by a great many writers about the effects of early experiences of human beings upon their subsequent personality development. Control in studies of children is far more difficult to achieve than in the case of animals. So it is not surprising that the total number of reliable findings is relatively small. Perhaps of the greatest interest have been studies of the effects of psychological deprivation in early childhood. These have been fully summarised and criticised in the reviews by Casler (1961) and by Yarrow (1961). We shall consider later in this chapter some of the studies in this field which appear to throw light on the lasting effects of exposure learning and possibly imprinting.

In distinguishing earlier in this chapter between the lasting effects of training and those of experiences which cannot be described as training we said nothing about the effects of imprinting. From the point of view of the character of its effects, early imprinting may be said to lie between training in the narrow sense and the more 'open' types of experience. One effect of imprinting is that attachment developed to a given figure, consisting of approach and following responses to the figure, later manifests itself in this very way; this is like simple training in that later behaviour is essentially a repetition of early behaviour. Another effect of imprinting, however, is that

9

attachment to the figure may later manifest itself in some new way, such as characteristic aggression towards, or courtship of the figure. Early exposure to the figure may also be responsible for the characteristic fears which the individual displays later in life. These lasting effects, if any, are not in the category of results of training.

We have already reviewed (see Chapter 4) the findings to-date concerning the effects of early imprinting upon the subsequent behaviour of the imprinted individuals. Our present-day knowledge of the lasting effects of imprinting in sub-human species is relatively less speculative than our knowledge of imprinting effects in human beings. Leaving for the moment human beings aside, three kinds of behaviour may be considered in animals: (1) shown preferences for particular features of the environment, (2) social behaviour, and (3) the choice of sexual objects.

Very little is known about the influence of imprinting upon the permanent preferences of animals for one or another kind of home environment. Indications of attachment to stationary features of environment were considered in Chapter 5. These were short-term manifestations of preference. Some of the attachments might prove to be durable on further investigation. One long-term effect of environmental exposure in birds was experimentally studied by Klopfer (1963). The subjects of his study were members of a passerine species, the chipping sparrow. Some individuals were reared without the sight of any foliage and some with oak foliage. These birds were later tested as adults, together with some wild-trapped adult birds, for choice of perch sites. Variables such as food, light intensity and perching opportunities were kept constant in the different groups under investigation. Klopfer found that wild adults preferred pine-tree to oak-tree sites. So did birds reared without any foliage, pine or oak. Those that had been reared in the presence of oak foliage chose almost equally between pine and oak perch sites. It may be wondered to what extent other species' preferences for habitats in adult life may be influenced by their infantile experiences.

As for the social behaviour of birds, Lorenz (1935) remarked that 'Innate social behaviour whose releaser must be acquired becomes dependent on the object of the young bird's world at a very definite stage in its development'. In the light of the studies of flocking quoted in Chapter 4 it is rather uncertain how influential the early developmental stages are. It is possible that early social experiences are more crucial for later social behaviour in some species than in others;

furthermore there is no doubt that socialisation brought about by instrumental learning may strengthen socialisation resulting from exposure (Scott, 1962). Further wide-ranging investigations into the long-term effects of imprinting upon the social behaviour of precocial animals are much needed.

Social consequences in rhesus monkeys of solitary rearing in infancy were investigated by Harlow and Harlow (1962). Monkeys deprived of the company of their peers between the third and sixth months of life were found to make poor social adjustment later in life. On the other hand, motherless infants reared together with other such infants were later capable of seemingly normal social interaction, even though, as the investigators pointed out, it was not possible to judge the final 'personality' development of these motherless, communally-reared individuals.

Lastly, it must be said that relatively little is known about the effects of early imprinting upon the sexual behaviour of animals. There is no doubt that sexual responses of birds can on occasions become 'misdirected' in accordance with the particular individual's imprinting experiences. Lack of suitable objects of attachment tends to result later in some cases in a distortion of social and sexual adjustment. Thus, Fisher and Hale (1957) showed that in the domestic fowl prolonged isolation from their own kind early in life could lead to misdirection of sexual responses. Kruijt (1962) demonstrated that it could also lead to an abnormal pattern of aggressive and escape behaviour.

However, Beach (1942) found that male rats kept in social isolation until maturity showed entirely normal sexual behaviour. Later, however, Kagan and Beach (1953) reported that the ejaculatory reactions in such rats were more frequent than in rats which had had some little previous experience of their own kind; see also Beach, 1955. Harlow and Harlow (1962) reported that monkeys reared in social isolation later showed quite abnormal sexual behaviour and seemed incapable of mating. And there were earlier reports that chimpanzees reared without heterosexual contacts were not capable of normal mating responses at maturity (Nissen, 1953). Thus, the influence of early experience on later sexual activity of mammals varies with species; again, there is scope for much further research in this area.

What rôle does imprinting play in personality development of human beings? Any attempted answer is highly speculative. Probably the first to make any specific suggestions was Gray (1958). He reviewed studies concerned with the smiling response, and studies of the effects of early deprivation and institutionalisation; he implied that imprinting might be the foundation of human personality development. It is open to doubt whether such a conclusion would be justifiable. And Gray did not attempt the formidable task of relating his suggestions about imprinting to the psychoanalytic position concerning the formative rôle of early experiences.

Some further speculations were offered by Hess (1962a). He proposed that 'the apathetic, nervous, or hostile behaviours manifested by orphanage children' were similar to the behaviour, said to be abnormal, of chicks reared in social isolation during the first few days after hatching. Salk (1962) was more concerned with the effects of certain experiences than with the effects of their absence. He ventured to say that 'music and dance are the result of imprinting and are created and experienced by man in his attempt to remain in proximity with imprinted stimuli'; music and dance would, thus, be unconscious attempts by man to recapture the sensory experiences similar to those 'received during prenatal life'. Needless to say, this is speculation in its purest form, incapable of being confirmed or refuted by any practicable observations or experiments.

Very rightly Hinde (1961) considered in a tentative manner some mammalian, and especially human, analogies of imprinting. A mother-figure is important in the life of young birds and mammals, including human infants. Precocial birds' early filial responses are at first non-specific, and through imprinting these animals become gradually attached to particular types of figure. Somewhat likewise, human filial responses, such as smiling and, later on, following, become gradually restricted to certain individuals. As Hinde points out, the development of fear of strangers, and of aggressive responses, seem to be similar in birds, anthropoids and human beings. The attachment of the child to its mother may well be influenced by physiological and derived rewards, but there is some evidence that it is rooted in the infant's initial unconditional responses to environmental stimuli, as are the attachments of imprinted precocial birds and precocial mammals, and of baby-monkeys, to their mother-figures.

We have seen earlier that there is evidence that the normal development of behaviour patterns in nidifugous birds requires the presence of a suitable object of imprinting early in the animal's life. The work of J. P. Scott and co-workers has shown that normal social development of such animals as sheep and dogs depends on early socialisation which is much more like imprinting than reward-and-punishment conditioning. Investigations by H. F. Harlow and co-workers have demonstrated that the company of a mother-figure and the company of sibling-figures are very important for the 'mental health' of a growing monkey. We may, next, wonder what could be the consequences of sensory and social deprivation of human infants.

It has been recognised for many years that any prolonged separation of the neonate from its mother tends to lead to a 'disorganisation' of the infant's personality (Ribble, 1946; see also Mussen et al., 1963). But it should not be assumed that lack of care and affection in infancy must inevitably have some dire effects on the child, as was to some extent implied in an early and influential book by Bowlby (1951). The contrary view, however, that the influence of such early adverse circumstances can be readily cancelled out later is implausible, partly because of the findings concerning the detrimental effects of a uniform, restricted and impoverished environment on growing animals. It could thus be reasonably expected that both a sensory monotony and a lack of stable social contact would tend to be detrimental to the normal development of children.

'Psychological deprivation' of a child brought up in an institution, unlike a normal home, was described and discussed, mainly from a psychoanalytic viewpoint, in a series of papers by Goldfarb; see, for example, Goldfarb, 1943, 1945. The personality of Goldfarb's 'institutionalised child' appeared to be much like the 'affectionless character', described by Bowlby. Later, Bowlby, Ainsworth, Boston and Rosenbluth (1956) set out to compare the effects of a prolonged stay in an institution with those of upbringing in an ordinary home environment. To carry out such a strictly controlled investigaton of institutionalisation was no mean undertaking. Children who had spent some months or years in a tuberculosis sanatorium before their fourth birthday were investigated when they were approximately seven to thirteen-and-a-half years. It was found that these children were rather more maladjusted, by the usual criteria, than comparable, control-group children. However, as the experimental children did not on the whole turn out to be delinquent, Bowlby and his colleagues concluded that 'statements implying that children who experience institutionalisation and similar forms of privation and deprivation in early life *commonly* develop psychopathic or affectionless characters are incorrect'.

To study the later behaviour of mother-attached and mother-separated children in terms of such gross effects as good social adjustment or maladjustment is one approach towards understanding the last-ing effects of the child's early experiences. Another approach is to analyse more closely the development of the child's ties to its mother and other people. Among the distinct responses which are initially made by the baby to the mother-figure Bowlby (1958, 1960a) recog-nised five: sucking, clinging, following, crying, smiling; these 'com-ponent instinctual responses' were considered by him to be evocable by certain appropriate stimuli. Bowlby suggested that attachment to mother is built upon these responses (see also Rheingold, 1961); he criticised the view that attachment to mother develops in the child as a result of reward learning, depending on the provision by the mother of food and creature comforts. This latter view stems from the tradi-tional type of learning theory; it is in keeping with the general pro-position well exemplified by the statement made by Dollard and Miller (1950), viz., '. . . probably the feeding experience can be the occasion for the child to learn to like to be with others; that is, it can establish the basis of sociability'.

However, as noted in the last chapter, feeding experience has been shown *not* to be the basis of sociability in puppies; see Brodbeck, 1954, Scott, 1962. Feeding experience has been shown *not* to be the basis of emotional ties of the baby-monkey to the mother-figure; see Harlow, 1958, 1959, etc. We can only guess that attachment to mother and socialisation of human children do not depend wholly on reward learning. It would appear that the upshot of Bowlby's analysis is that (1) the learning of the characteristics of the mother comes about as a result of exposure to her, and (2) the development of attachment is basically an imprinting-like process.

One of the 'component instinctual responses', smiling, has been studied quite extensively. Ahrens (1954) considered early smiling responses to be innately determined and releasable by appropriate stimuli. Salzen (1963b) showed that earlier findings (such as those of Spitz and Wolfe, 1946) concerning the nature of the releasing stimuli could not be accepted in their entirety. Bowlby (1957) thought of smiling as being released in the ethological sense; and he expressed disagreement with Spitz who had earlier considered smiling to be learned instrumentally.

A child needs time to acquire the ability to differentiate his mother from other people; he cannot be shown to know his mother before the age of about six months. A child cannot, strictly speaking, experience maternal loss or deprivation before he knows his mother, although the loss of stimulation provided by adults could well result in certain changes in the child's behaviour. Observations of infants under one year of age in hospital surroundings led Schaffer (1958) to recognise two phases of deprivation: perceptual deprivation in the very young babies, and maternal deprivation in those babies that had shown signs of knowing their mothers. Such symptoms of deprivation as were observed in the early 'global stage' – as Schaffer called it – indicated symptoms of deficiency of stimulation (Ribble, 1946, talked earlier about infants' 'hunger' for stimulation). Only during the later, 'differentiated stage' could Schaffer observe the usual symptoms of mother-separation in the strict sense. Bowlby (1960a, b) concerned himself with such symptoms, and discerned three stages in the child's reaction to separation which he labelled: protest, despair, and detachment.

Thus, as Bowlby (1962) sees it, during the first six months or so of his life the child faces the impact of sensory stimulation, and learns to recognise against the environmental background 'a particular figure usually his mother'. In the process the child develops an attachment to his mother which continues to grow stronger and stronger with time. It is possible that a systematic, profitable exploration of the environment by the child can begin only when a secure bond of this kind has been created. Certainly Harlow's monkeys explore the environment most effectively when they can 'fall back' upon a secure relationship with a mother-figure.

It is at present a matter for speculation whether indications of venturesomeness in human beings go together with certain signs of 'emotional security'; further personality research should provide an answer. Likewise, we can only wonder whether attachment to one's own home environment, or even one's country, does in any way depend on some form of imprinting. It has been said that a man's choice of his wife could be influenced by the early impact of his mother's personality and appearance. Perhaps imprinting-like early learning is also a factor in adult homosexuality and in paedophilia (sexual love of children by adults, as described, for instance, in the novel *Lolita* by Nabokov).

It would be very unwise to look for the roots of human personality traits, abnormal and normal, mainly in certain kinds of early experience, thereby neglecting the full range of personality determinants in man's inheritance and environment. Nevertheless, the relatively unrecognised rôle of imprinting-like early learning could and should now be more closely considered. The need at present is to gain much more factual knowledge about all aspects of imprinting-like processes. Only then will it be possible to understand more clearly the contribution of imprinting to both ordinary and uncommon behaviour.

\*

'The souls of little children are marvellously delicate and tender things, and keep for ever the shadow that first falls on them. . ..' Olive Schreiner (1883): *The Story of an African Farm.*

# REFERENCES

ABERCROMBIE, B. & JAMES, H. (1961). The stability of the domestic chick's response to visual flicker. *Anim. Behav.*, **9**, 205–212.

AHRENS, R. (1954). Beitrag zur Entwicklung des Physiognomie- und Mimikerkennes. *Z. Exp. Angew. Psychol.*, **2**, Part I: 412–454; Part II: 599–633.

ALLEY, R. & BOYD, H. (1950). Parent–young recognition in the coot. *Ibis*, **92**, 46–51.

ALTMANN, M. (1958). Social integration in the moose calf. *Anim. Behav.*, **6**, 155–159.

BAER, D. M. & GRAY, P. H. (1960). Imprinting to a different species without overt following. *Percept. Mot. Skills*, **10**, 171–174.

BAERENDS, G. P. & BAERENDS-VAN ROON, J. M. (1950) *An Introduction to the Study of the Ethology of Cichlid Fishes* (*Behaviour Supplement I*, 1–243). Leiden: Brill.

BAMBRIDGE, R. (1962). Early experience and sexual behaviour in the domestic chicken. *Science*, **136**, 259–260.

BARNETT, S. A. (1958). Exploratory behaviour. *Brit. J. Psychol.* **49**, 289–310.

BARON, A. & KISH, G. B. (1960). Early social isolation as a determinant of aggregative behavior in the domestic chicken. *J. comp. physiol. Psychol.*, **53**, 459–463.

BARON, A., KISH, G. B. & ANTONITIS, J. J. (1961). Stimulus determinants of aggregative behavior in the domestic chicken. *J. genet. Psychol.*, **98**, 177–182.

(1962). Effects of early and late social isolation on aggregative behavior in the domestic chicken. *J. genet. Psychol.*, **100**, 355–360.

BEACH, F. A. (1942). Comparison of copulatory behavior of male rats raised in isolation, cohabitation and segregation. *J. genet. Psychol.*, **60**, 121–136.

(1955). Ontogeny and living systems. In: Schaffner, B. (Ed.). *Group Processes*. New York: Macy Foundation.

BEACH, F. A. & JAYNES, J. (1954). Effects of early experience upon the behavior of animals. *Psychol. Bull.*, **51**, 239–263.

BEXTON, W. H., HERON, W. & SCOTT, T. H. (1954). Effects of decreased variation in the sensory environment. *Canad. J. Psychol.*, **8**, 70–76.

BIEL, W. C. (1940). Early age differences in maze performance in the albino rat. *J. genet. Psychol.*, **56**, 439–453.

BINDRA, D. (1959). *Motivation.* New York: Ronald Press.

BINGHAM, W. E. & GRIFFITHS, W. J. (1952). The effect of different environments during infancy on adult behavior in the rat. *J. comp. physiol. Psychol.*, **45**, 307–312.

BOWLBY, J. (1951). *Maternal Care and Mental Health.* Geneva: World Health Organization Monograph Series.

(1953). Based on the above: *Child Care and the Growth of Love.* London: Penguin Books.

(1957). Symposium on the contribution of current theories to an understanding of child development. I. An ethological approach to research in child development. *Brit. J. med. Psychol.*, **30**, 230–240.

(1958). The nature of the child's tie to his mother. *Internat. J. Psycho-anal.*, **39**, 1–24.

(1960a). Separation anxiety. *Internat. J. Psycho-anal.*, **41**, 89–113.

(1960b). Grief and mourning in infancy and early childhood. *Psychoanal. Study Child.*, **15**, 9–52.

(1962). Childhood bereavement and psychiatric illness. In: Richter, D. *et al.* (Eds.) *Aspects of Psychiatric Research.* London: Oxford University Press.

BOWLBY, J., AINSWORTH, M., BOSTON, M. & ROSENBLUTH, D. (1956). The effects of mother-child separation: a follow-up study. *Brit. J. med. Psychol.*, **29**, 211–247.

BRETT, G. S. (1912, 1921). *A History of Psychology.* London: Allen & Unwin.

BROADBENT, D. E. (1961). *Behaviour.* London: Eyre & Spottiswoode.

BRODBECK, A. J. (1954). An exploratory study on the acquisition of dependency behavior in puppies. *Bull. Ecol. Soc. Am.*, **35**, 73.

BUGELSKI, B. R. (1956). *The Psychology of Learning.* New York: Holt.

BUTLER, R. A. (1953). Discrimination learning in rhesus monkeys to visual-exploration motivation. *J. comp. physiol. Psychol.*, **46**, 95–98.

(1954). Incentive conditions which influence visual exploration. *J. exp. Psychol.*, **48**, 19–23.

CAMPBELL, B. A. & PICKLEMAN, J. R. (1961). The imprinting object as a reinforcing stimulus. *J. comp. physiol. Psychol.*, **54**, 592–596.

CANDLAND, D. K. & CAMPBELL, B. A. (1962). Development of fear in the rat as measured by behavior in the open field. *J. comp. physiol. Psychol.*, **55**, 593–596.

CARR, H. A. (Ed.) (1919). *Orthogenetic Evolution of Pigeons*: *Vol.* 3. Washington: Carnegie Institution. See also Whitman (1919).

CASLER, L. (1961). Maternal deprivation: a critical review of the literature. *Monogr. Soc. Res. Child Developm.*, **26**, No. 2.

COFOID, D. A. & HONIG, W. K. (1961). Stimulus generalization of imprinting. *Science*, **134**, 1692–1694.

COLLIAS, N. E. (1952). The development of social behavior in birds. *Auk*, **69**, 127–159.

(1962). Social development in birds and mammals. In: Bliss, E. L. (Ed.). *Roots of Behavior*. New York: Harper & Bros.

COLLIAS, N. E. & COLLIAS, E. C. (1956). Some mechanisms of family integration in ducks. *Auk*, **73**, 378–400.

COLLIAS, N. E. & JOOS, M. (1953). The spectrographic analysis of sound signals of the domestic fowl. *Behaviour*, **5**, 175–188.

CRAIG, W. (1908). The voices of pigeons regarded as a means of social control. *Amer. J. Sociol.*, **14**, 86–100.

(1914). Male doves reared in isolation. *J. Anim. Behav.*, **4**, 121–133.

CUSHING, J. E. & RAMSAY, A. O. (1949). The non-heritable aspects of family unity in birds. *Condor*, **51**, 82–87.

DEMBER, W. N. & EARL, R. W. (1957). Analysis of exploratory, manipulatory and curiosity behaviors. *Psychol. Rev.*, **64**, 91–96.

DENENBERG, V. H. (1959). The interactive effects of infantile and adult shock levels upon learning. *Psychol. Rep.*, **5**, 357–364.

(1962). The effects of early experience. In: Hafez, E. S. E. (Ed.). *The Behaviour of Domestic Animals*. London: Ballière, Tindall & Cox.

DENENBERG, V. H. & BELL, R. W. (1960). Critical periods for the effects of infantile experience on adult learning. *Science*, **131**, 227–228.

DENENBERG, V. H. & KARAS, G. G. (1960). Interactive effects of age and duration of infantile experience on adult learning. *Psychol. Rep.*, **7**, 313–322.

DOLLARD, J. & MILLER, N. E. (1950). *Personality and Psychotherapy*. New York: McGraw-Hill.

FABRICIUS, E. (1951a). Zur Ethologie junger Anatiden. *Acta Zool. Fenn.*, **68**, 1–175.

(1951b). Some experiments on imprinting phenomena in ducks. *Proc. X Internat. Ornithol. Congr.*, 375–379.

(1955). Experiments on the following-reponse of mallard ducklings. *Brit. J. Anim. Behav.*, **3**, 122.

(1962). Some aspects of imprinting in birds. *Symp. zoo. Soc. Lond.*, **8**, 139–148.

FABRICIUS, E. & BOYD, H. (1954). Experiments on the following reactions of ducklings. *Wildfowl Trust ann. Rep. (1952/53)*, **6**, 84–89.

FANTZ, R. L. (1957). Form preferences in newly hatched chicks. *J. comp. physiol. Psychol.*, **50**, 422–430.

FISHER, E. A. & HALE, E. B. (1957). Stimulus determinants of sexual and aggressive behaviour in male domestic fowl. *Behaviour*, **10**, 309–323.

FORGAYS, D. G. & FORGAYS, J. W. (1952). The nature of the effect of free-environmental experience in the rat. *J. comp. physiol. Psychol.*, **45**, 322–328.

FORGAYS, D. G. & READ, J. M. (1962). Crucial periods for free-environmental experience in the rat. *J. comp. physiol. Psychol.*, **55**, 816–818.

FORGUS, R. H. (1954). The effect of early perceptual learning on the behavioral organization of adult rats. *J. comp. physiol. Psychol.*, **47**, 331–336.

(1955). Early visual and motor experience as determiners of complex maze-learning ability under rich and reduced stimulation. *J. comp. physiol. Psychol.*, **48**, 215–220.

FOSS, B. M. (Ed.) (1961). *Determinants of Infant Behaviour. Vol. I.* London: Methuen.

FRISCH, O. V. (1957). Mit einem Purpurreiher verheiratet. *Z. Tierpsychol.*, **14**, 233–237.

GIBSON, E. J. & WALK, R. D. (1956). The effect of prolonged exposure to visually presented patterns on learning to discriminate them. *J. comp. physiol. Psychol.*, **49**, 239–242.

GIBSON, E. J., WALK, R. D., PICK, H. L. JR. & TIGHE, T. J. (1958). The effect of prolonged exposure to visual patterns on learning to discriminate similar and different patterns. *J. comp. physiol. Psychol.*, **51**, 584–587.

GIBSON, J. J. & GIBSON, E. J. (1955). Perceptual learning: differentiation and enrichment. *Psychol. Rev.*, **62**, 32–41.

GLANZER, M. (1958). Curiosity, exploratory drive, and stimulus satiation. *Psychol. Bull.*, **55**, 302–315.

GOLDFARB, W. (1943). Effects of early institutional care on adolescent personality. *J. exp. Educ.*, **12**, 106–129.

(1945). Effects of psychological deprivation in infancy and subsequent stimulation. *Amer. J. Psychiat.*, **102**, 18–33.

GOODWIN, D. (1948). Some abnormal sexual fixations in birds. *Ibis*, **90**, 45–48.

GOTTLIEB, G. (1961a). Developmental age as a baseline for determination of the critical period in imprinting. *J. comp. physiol. Psychol.*, **54**, 422–427.

(1961b). The following-response and imprinting in wild and domestic ducklings of the same species. *Behaviour*, **18**, 205–228.

(1963a). 'Imprinting' in nature. *Science*, **139**, 497–498.

(1963b). A naturalistic study of imprinting in wood ducklings (*aix sponsa*). *J. comp. physiol. Psychol.*, **56**, 86–91.

(1963c). Following-response initiation in ducklings: age and sensory stimulation. *Science*, **140**, 399–400.

GOTTLIEB, G. & KLOPFER, P. H. (1962). The relation of developmental age to auditory and visual imprinting. *J. comp. physiol. Psychol.*, **55**, 821–826.

GRABOWSKI, U. (1941). Prägung eines Jungschafs auf den Menschen. *Z. Tierpsychol.*, **4**, 326-329.

GRAY, P. H. (1958). Theory and evidence of imprinting in human infants. *J. Psychol.*, **46**, 155–166.

(1960). Evidence that retinal flicker is not a necessary condition of imprinting. *Science*, **132**, 1834.

(1961a). Imprinting. *Science*, **133**, 924–928.

(1961b). The releasers of imprinting: differential reactions to color as a function of maturation. *J. comp. physiol. Psychol.*, **54**, 597–601.

(1962). Is the imprinting critical period an artifact of a biological clock. *Percept. Mot. Skills*, **14**, 70.

GRAY, P. H. & HOWARD, K. I. (1957). Specific recognition of humans in imprinted chicks. *Percept. Mot. Skills*, **7**, 301–304.

GREENBERG, B. (1963a). Parental behaviour and imprinting in cichlid fishes. *Behaviour*, **21**, 127–144.

(1963b). Parental behaviour and recognition of young in *Cichlasoma biocellatum*. *Anim. Behav.*, **11**, 578–582.

GUHL, A. M. (1962). The behaviour of chickens. In: Hafez, E. S. E. (Ed.). *The Behaviour of Domestic Animals*. London: Baillière, Tindall & Cox.

GUITON, P. (1958). The effect of isolation on the following response of Brown Leghorn chicks. *Proc. roy. phys. Soc. Edinb.*, **27**, 9–14.

(1959). Socialisation and imprinting in Brown Leghorn chicks. *Anim. Behav.*, **7**, 26–34.

(1961). The influence of imprinting on the agonistic and courtship responses of the Brown Leghorn cock. *Anim. Behav.*, **9**, 167–177.

(1962). The development of sexual responses in the domestic fowl in relation to the concept of imprinting. *Symp. zoo. Soc. Lond., No. 8*, 227–234.

HALE, E. B. & SCHEIN, M. W. (1962). The behaviour of turkeys. In: Hafez, E. S. E. (Ed.). *The Behaviour of Domestic Animals*. London: Baillière, Tindall & Cox.

HARLOW, H. F. (1949). The formation of learning sets. *Psychol. Rev.*, **56**, 51–65.

(1950). Learning and satiation of response in intrinsically motivated complex puzzle performance in monkeys. *J. comp. physiol. Psychol.*, **43**, 289–294.

(1953a). Mice, monkeys, men and motives. *Psychol. Rev.*, **60**, 23–32.

(1953b). Motivation as a factor in the acquisition of new responses. In: Brown, J. S. et al. (Eds.). *Current Theory and Research in Motivation*. Lincoln, Neb.: University of Nebraska Press.

(1958). The nature of love. *Amer. Psychologist*, **13**, 673–685.

(1959). Love in infant monkeys. *Sci. Amer.*, **200**, 68–74.

(1960). Primary affectional patterns in primates. *Amer. J. Orthopsychiat.*, **30**, 676–684.

(1961). The development of affectional patterns in infant monkeys. In: Foss, B. M. (Ed.). *Determinants of Infant Behaviour. Vol. I.* London: Methuen.

(1962). Development of affection in primates. In: Bliss, E. L. (Ed.). *Roots of Behavior*. New York: Harper & Bros.

HARLOW, H. F. & HARLOW, M. K. (1962). Social deprivation in monkeys. *Sci. Amer.*, **207**, 137–146.

HARLOW, H. F., HARLOW, M. K. & MEYER, D. R. (1950). Learning motivated by a manipulation drive. *J. exp. Psychol.*, **40**, 228–234.

HARLOW, H. F. & MCCLEARN, G. E. (1954). Object discrimination learned by monkeys on the basis of manipulation motives. *J. comp. physiol. Psychol.*, **47**, 73–76.

HARLOW, H. F. & ZIMMERMANN, R. R. (1958). The development of affectional responses in infant monkeys. *Proc. Amer. Phil. Soc.*, **102**, 501–509.

(1959). Affectional responses in the infant monkey. *Science*, **130**, 421–432.

HAYES, W. N. & WARREN, J. M. (1963). Failure to find spontaneous alternation in chicks. *J. comp. physiol. Psychol.*, **56**, 575–577.

HEBB, D. O. (1946). On the nature of fear. *Psychol. Rev.*, **53**, 250–275.
(1949). *The Organization of Behavior.* New York: Wiley.
HEBB, D. O., HEATH, E. S. & STUART, E. A. (1954). Experimental deafness. *Canad. J. Psychol.*, **8**, 152–156.
HEDIGER, H. (1950). *Wild Animals in Captivity.* London: Butterworth.
(1955). *Studies of the Psychology and Behaviour of Captive Animals in Zoos and Circuses.* London: Butterworth.
HEINROTH, O. (1911). Beiträge zur Biologie, nahmentlich Ethologie und Psychologie der Anatiden. *Verh. 5 int. orn. Kongr. Berlin, 1910*, 589–702.
HEINROTH, O. & HEINROTH, K. (1959). *The Birds.* London: Faber & Faber.
HERON, W., DOANE, B. K. & SCOTT, T. H. (1956). Visual disturbances after prolonged perceptual isolation. *Canad. J. Psychol.*, **10**, 13–18.
HERSHER, L., RICHMOND, J. B. & MOORE, A. V. (1963). Modifiability of the critical period for the development of maternal behaviour in sheep and goats. *Behaviour*, **20**, 311–320.
HESS, E. H. (1956). Natural preferences of chicks and ducklings for objects of different colours. *Psychol. Rep.*, **2**, 477–483.
(1957). Effects of meprobamate on imprinting in water-fowl. *Ann. N.Y. Acad. Sci.*, **67**, 724–732.
(1958). 'Imprinting' in animals. *Sci. Amer.*, **198**, 81–90.
(1959a). Imprinting. *Science*, **130**, 133–141.
(1959b). The conditions limiting critical age of imprinting. *J. comp. physiol. Psychol.*, **52**, 515–518.
(1959c). The relationship between imprinting and motivation. In: Jones, M. R. (Ed.). *Nebraska Symposium on Motivation.* Lincoln, Neb.: University of Nebraska Press.
(1962a). Imprinting and the 'critical period' concept. In: Bliss, E. L. (Ed.). *Roots of Behavior.* New York: Harper & Bros.
(1962b). Ethology: an approach toward the complete analysis of behavior. In: Brown, R., Galanter, E., Hess, E. H. and Mandler, G. *New Directions in Psychology.* New York: Holt, Rinehart & Winston.
HESS, E. H. & GOGEL, W. C. (1954). Natural preferences of the chick for objects of different colors. *J. Psychol.*, **38**, 483–493.
HESS, E. H., POLT, J. M. & GODWIN, E. (1959). Effects of carisoprodol on early experience in learning. In: Miller, J. G. (Ed.). *The Pharmacology and Clinical Uses of Carisoprodol.* Detroit: Wayne State University Press.

HESS, E. H. & SCHAEFER, H. H. (1959). Innate behavior patterns as indicators of the 'critical period'. *Z. Tierpsychol.*, **16**, 155–160.

HILGARD, E. R. & MARQUIS, D. G. (1961). *Conditioning and Learning.* London: Methuen.

HINDE, R. A. (1955a). The modifiability of instinctive behaviour. *Adv. Sci.*, **12**, 19–24.

(1955b). The following response of moorhens and coots. *Brit. J. Anim. Behav.*, **3**, 121–122.

(1959). Some recent trends in ethology. In: Koch, S. (Ed.). *Psychology: A Study of Science: Vol. 2.* New York: McGraw-Hill.

(1961). The establishment of the parent-offspring relation in birds, with some mammalian analogies. In: Thorpe, W. H. and Zangwill, O. L. (Eds.). *Current Problems in Animal Behaviour.* Cambridge: C.U.P.

(1962a). The relevance of animal studies to human neurotic disorders. In: Richter, D. *et al.* (Eds.). *Aspects of Psychiatric Research.* London: Oxford University Press.

(1962b). Some aspects of the imprinting problem. *Sym. zoo. Soc. Lond.*, *No. 8*, 129–138.

HINDE, R. A., THORPE, W. H. & VINCE, M. A. (1956). The following response of young coots and moorhens. *Behaviour*, **11**, 214–242.

HYMOVITCH, B. (1952). The effects of experimental variation on problem solving in rats. *J. comp. physiol. Psychol.*, **45**, 313–320.

JAMES, H. (1959). Flicker: an unconditioned stimulus for imprinting. *Canad. J. Psychol.*, **13**, 59–67.

(1960a). Imprinting with visual flicker: evidence for a critical period. *Canad. J. Psychol.*, **14**, 13–20.

(1960b). Social inhibition of the domestic chick's response to visual flicker. *Anim. Behav.*, **8**, 223–224.

(1960c). Imprinting. *Ontario psychol. Assoc. Quarterly*, **13**, 41–74.

(1961). Personal communication.

JAMES, H. & BINKS, C. (1963). Escape and avoidance learning in newly hatched domestic chicks. *Science*, **139**, 1293–1294.

JAMES, W. (1890). *Principles of Psychology.* New York: Holt.

JAYNES, J. (1956). Imprinting: the interaction of learned and innate behaviour. I. Development and generalization. *J. comp. physiol. Psychol.*, **49**, 201–206.

(1957). Imprinting: the interaction of learned and innate behavior. II. The critical period. *J. comp. physiol. Psychol.*, **50**, 6–10.

(1958a). Imprinting: the interaction of learned and innate behavior: III. Practice effects on performance, retention and fear. *J. comp. physiol. Psychol.*, **51**, 234–237.

(1958b). Imprinting: the interaction of learned and innate behavior: IV. Generalization and emergent discrimination. *J. comp. physiol. Psychol.*, **51**, 238–242.

KAGAN, J. & BEACH, F. A. (1953). Effects of early experience on mating behavior of male rats. *J. comp. phsyiol. Psychol.*, **46**, 204–208.

KANTROW, R. W. (1937). An investigation of conditioned feeding responses and concomitant adaptive behavior in young infants. *Univ. Iowa Stud. Child Welfare*, **13**, No. 3.

KAUFMAN, I. C. & HINDE, R. A. (1961). Factors influencing distress calling in chicks, with special reference to temperature changes in social isolation. *Anim. Behav.*, **9**, 197–204.

KEAR, J. (1960). Abnormal sexual behaviour of a hawfinch. *Ibis*, **102**, 614–616.

KING, J. A. (1958). Parameters relevant to determining the effect of early experience upon the adult behavior of animals. *Psychol. Bull.*, **55**, 46–58.

KLOPFER, P. H. (1956). Comments concerning the age at which imprinting occurs. *Wilson Bull.*, **68**, 320–321.

(1959a). An analysis of learning in young anatidae. *Ecology*, **40**, 90–102.

(1959b). The development of sound-signal preferences in ducks. *Wilson. Bull.*, **71**, 262–266.

(1961). Imprinting. *Science*, **133**, 923–924.

(1963). Behavioral aspects of habitat selection: the rôle of early experience. *Wilson Bull.*, **75**, 15–22.

KLOPFER, P. H. & GOTTLIEB, G. (1962a). Imprinting and behavioral polymorphism: auditory and visual imprinting in domestic ducks and the involvement of the critical period. *J. comp. physiol. Psychol.*, **55**, 126–130.

(1962b). Learning ability and behavioral polymorphism within individual clutches of wild ducklings (*anas platyrhynchos*). *Z. Tierpsychol.*, **19**, 183–190.

KOVACH, J. K. & HESS, E. H. (1963). Imprinting: effects of painful stimulation upon the following response. *J. comp. physiol. Psychol.*, **56**, 461–464.

KRUIJT, J. P. (1962). Imprinting in relation to drive interactions in Burmese Red Junglefowl. *Sym. zoo. Soc. Lond.*, No. 8, 219–226.

10

LEROY, C. G. (1870). *The Intelligence and Perfectibility of Animals from a Philosophic Point of View.* London: Chapman & Hall.

LEVINE, S. (1956). A further study of infantile handling and adult avoidance learning. *J. Personality,* **25,** 70–80.

(1962a). The effects of infantile experience on adult behavior. In: Bachrach, A. J. (Ed.). *Experimental Foundations of Clinical Psychology.* New York: Basic Books.

(1962b). Psychological effect of infantile stimulation. In: Bliss, E. L. (Ed.). *Roots of Behavior.* New York: Harper & Bros.

LEVINE, S., CHEVALIER, J. A. & KORCHIN, S. J. (1956). The effects of early shock and handling on later avoidance learning. *J. Personality,* **24,** 475–493.

LORENZ, K. (1935). Der Kumpan in der Umwelt des Vogels; die Artgenosse als auslösendes Moment sozialer Verhaltungsweisen. *J. Ornithol.,* **83,** 137–213 and 289–413. Also in English translation under the title 'Companionship in bird life; fellow members of the species as releasers of social behavior', in: Schiller, C. H. (Ed.) (1957). *Instinctive Behavior.* New York: Intern. University Press.

(1937a). Über die Bildung des Instinktbegriffes. *Naturwissenschaften,* **25,** 289–300, 307–318 and 324–331. Also in English translation under the title 'The nature of instinct', in: Schiller, C. H. (Ed.) (1957). *Instinctive Behavior.* New York: Intern. University Press.

(1937b). The companion in the bird's world. *Auk,* **54,** 245–273.

(1952). *King Solomon's Ring.* London: Methuen.

(1955). Morphology and behavior patterns in closely allied species. In: Schaffner, B. (Ed.). *Group Processes.* New York: Macy Foundation.

LURIA, A. R. (1932). *The Nature of Human Conflicts.* New York: Liveright.

MACE, C. A. (1962). Psychology and aesthetics. *Brit. J. Aesthet.,* **2,** 3–16.

MELZACK, R. (1952). Irrational fears in the dog. *Canad. J. Psychol.,* **6,** 141–147.

MENZEL, JR., E. W. (1963). The effects of cumulative experience on responses to novel objects in young isolation-reared chimpanzees. *Behaviour,* **21,** 1–12.

MILES, R. C. (1958). Learning in kittens with manipulatory, exploratory, and food incentives. *J. comp. physiol. Psychol.,* **51,** 39–42.

MILLER, N. E. (1948). Studies of fear as an acquirable drive: I. Fear as motivation and fear-reduction as reinforcement in the learning of new responses. *J. exp. Psychol.*, **38**, 89–101.

(1951). Learnable drives and rewards. In: Stevens, S. S. (Ed.). *Handbook of Experimental Psychology*. New York: Wiley.

MOLTZ, H. (1960). Imprinting: empirical basis and theoretical significance. *Psychol. Bull.*, **57**, 291–314.

(1961). Retinal flicker and imprinting. *Science*, **133**, 970.

(1963). Imprinting: an epigenetic approach. *Psychol. Rev.*, **70**, 123–138.

MOLTZ, H. & ROSENBLUM, L. A. (1958a). Imprinting and associative learning: the stability of the following response in Peking ducks. *J. comp. physiol. Psychol.*, **51**, 580–583.

(1958b). The relation between habituation and the stability of the following response. *J. comp. physiol. Psychol.*, **51**, 658–661.

MOLTZ, H., ROSENBLUM, L. & HALIKAS, N. (1959). Imprinting and level of anxiety. *J. comp. physiol. Psychol.*, **52**, 240–244.

MOLTZ, H., ROSENBLUM, L. & STETTNER, L. J. (1960). Some parameters of imprinting effectiveness. *J. comp. physiol. Psychol.*, **53**, 297–301.

MOLTZ, H. & STETTNER, L. J. (1961). The influence of patterned-light deprivation on the critical period for imprinting. *J. comp. physiol. Psychol.*, **54**, 279–283.

MONTGOMERY, K. C. (1951). The relation between exploratory behavior and spontaneous alternation in the white rat. *J. comp. physiol. Psychol.*, **44**, 582–589.

(1954). The rôle of the exploratory drive in learning. *J. comp. physiol. Psychol.*, **47**, 60–64.

(1955). The relation between fear induced by novel stimulation and exploratory behavior. *J. comp. physiol. Psychol.*, **48**, 254–260.

MORGAN, C. T. (1961). *Introduction to Psychology*. New York: McGraw-Hill.

MOWRER, O. H. (1939). A stimulus-response analysis of anxiety and its rôle as a reinforcing agent. *Psychol. Rev.*, **46**, 553–565.

(1960). *Learning Theory and Behavior*. New York: Wiley.

MUNN, N. L. (1950). *Handbook of Psychological Research on the Rat*. Boston: Houghton Mifflin.

(1954). Learning in children. In: Carmichael, L. (Ed.). *Manual of Child Psychology*. New York: Wiley.

MURPHY, G. (1947). *Personality: A Biosocial Approach to Origins and Structure.* New York: Harper & Bros.

(1960). *Human Potentialities.* London: Allen & Unwin.

MUSSEN, P. H., CONGER, J. J. & KAGAN, J. (1963). *Child Development and Personality.* New York: Harper & Row.

NICE, M. M. (1950). Development of a redwing (*Agelaius phoeniceus*). *Wilson Bull.*, **62**, 87–93.

(1953). Some experiences in imprinting ducklings. *Condor*, **55**, 33–37.

NICOLAI, J. (1956). Zur Biologie und Ethologie des Gimpels. *Z. Tierpsychol.*, **13**, 93–132.

NISSEN, H. W. (1953). Instinct as seen by a psychologist. *Psychol. Rev.*, **60**, 291–294.

(1954). The nature of the drive as innate determinant of behavioral organization. In: Jones, M. R. (Ed.). *Nebraska Symposium on Motivation.* Lincoln, Neb.: University of Nebraska Press.

PATTIE, JR. F. A. (1936). The gregarious behavior of normal chicks and chicks hatched in isolation. *J. comp. Psychol.*, **21**, 161–178.

PETERS, R. S. (Ed.) (1953). *Brett's History of Psychology.* London: Allen & Unwin.

PITZ, G. F. & ROSS, R. B. (1961). Imprinting as a function of arousal. *J. comp. physiol. Psychol.*, **54**, 602–604.

PUMPHREY, R. J. (1948). The sense organs of birds. *Ibis*, **90**, 171–199.

(1961). Sensory organs. In: Marshall, A. J. (Ed.). *Biology and Comparative Physiology of Birds.* New York: Academic Press.

RÄBER, H. (1948). Analyse des Balzverhaltens eines domestizierten Truthans. *Behaviour*, **1**, 237–266.

RAMSAY, A. O. (1951). Familial recognition in domestic birds. *Auk*, **68**, 1–16.

RAMSAY, A. O. & HESS, E. H. (1954). A laboratory approach to the study of imprinting. *Wilson Bull.*, **66**, 196–206.

RATNER, S. C. & THOMPSON, R. W. (1960). Immobility reactions (fear) of domestic fowl as a function of age and prior experience. *Anim. Behav.*, **8**, 186–191.

RHEINGOLD, H. L. (1961). The effect of environmental stimulation upon social and exploratory behaviour in the human infant. In: Foss, B. M. (Ed.). *Determinants of Infant Behaviour. Vol. I.* London: Methuen.

RIBBLE, M. A. (1946). Disorganizing factors in infant personality. In: Tomkins, S. S. (Ed.). *Contemporary Psychopathology*, Cambridge, Mass.: Harvard University Press.

RICE, C. E. (1962). Imprinting by force. *Science*, **138**, 680–681.

RIESEN, A. H. (1961). Studying perceptual development using the technique of sensory deprivation. *J. nerv. ment. Dis.*, **132**, 21–25.

RUSSELL, W. R. (1959). *Brain, Memory, Learning*. Oxford: Clarendon Press.

SALK, L. (1962). Mothers' heartbeat as an imprinting stimulus. *Trans. N. Y. Acad. Sc.*, **24**, 753–763.

SALZEN, E. A. (1962). Imprinting and Fear. *Symp. zoo. Soc. Lond.*, *No. 8*, 197–217.

(1963a). Imprinting and the immobility reactions of domestic fowl. *Anim. Behav.*, **11**, 66–71.

(1963b). Visual stimuli eliciting the smiling response in the human infant. *J. genet. Psychol.*, **102**, 51–54.

SALZEN, E. A. & SLUCKIN, W. (1959a). An experiment in imprinting domestic fowl. *Bull. Brit. psychol. Soc.*, *No. 38*, 35A–36A.

(1959b). The incidence of the following response and the duration of responsiveness in domestic fowl. *Anim. Behav.*, **7**, 172–179.

SALZEN, E. A. & TOMLIN, F. J. (1963). The effect of cold on the following response of domestic fowl. *Anim. Behav.*, **11**, 62–65.

SCHAEFER, H. H. & HESS, E. H. (1959). Color preferences in imprinting object. *Z. Tierpsychol.*, **16**, 161–172.

SCHAFFER, H. R. (1958). Objective observations of personality development in early infancy. *Brit. J. med. Psychol.*, **31**, 174–183.

SCHALLER, G. B. & EMLEN, J. T. (1962). The ontogeny of avoidance behaviour in some precocial birds. *Anim. Behav.*, **10**, 370–381.

SCHEIN, M. W. & HALE, E. B. (1959). The effect of early social experience on male sexual behaviour of androgen injected turkeys. *Anim. Behav.*, **7**, 189–200.

SCHNEIRLA, T. C. (1956). Interrelationships of the 'innate' and the 'acquired' in instinctive behavior. In: *L'Instinct dans le Comportement des Animaux et de l'Homme*. Paris: Masson & Cie.

(1959). An evolutionary and developmental theory of biphasic processes underlying approach and withdrawal. In: Jones, M. R. (Ed.). *Nebraska Symposium on Motivation*. Lincoln, Neb.: University of Nebraska Press.

SCHOOLAND, J. B. (1942). Are there any innate behavior tendencies? *Genet. Psychol. Monogr.*, **25**, 219–287.

SCOTT, J. P. (1945). Social behavior, organization and leadership in a small flock of domestic sheep. *Comp. Psychol. Monogr.*, **18**, 1–29.

(1958a). *Animal Behavior*. Chicago: University of Chicago Press.

(1958b). Critical periods in the development of social behavior in puppies. *Psychosom. Med.*, **20**, 42–54.

(1962). Critical periods in behavioral development. *Science*, **138**, 949–958.

SCOTT, J. P., FREDERICSON, E. & FULLER, J. L. (1951). Experimental exploration of the critical period hypothesis. *Personality*, **1**, 162–183.

SCOTT, J. P. & MARSTON, M. V. (1950). Critical periods affecting the development of normal and mal-adjustive social behavior in puppies. *J. genet. Psychol.*, **77**, 25–60.

SHIPLEY, W. U. (1963). The demonstration in the domestic guinea pig of a process resembling classical imprinting. *Anim. Behav.*, **11**, 470–474.

SIEGEL, A. I. (1953). Deprivation of visual form definition in the ring dove. I. Discriminatory learning. *J. comp. physiol. Psychol.*, **46**, 115–119.

SLUCKIN, W. (1960). Towards a theory of filial responses. *Bull. Brit. psychol. Soc.*, *No. 40*, 5A.

(1962). Perceptual and associative learning. *Symp. zoo. Soc. Lond.*, *No. 8*, 193–198.

SLUCKIN, W. & SALZEN, E. A. (1961). Imprinting and perceptual learning. *Quart. J. exp. Psychol.*, **13**, 65–77.

SLUCKIN, W. & TAYLOR, K. F. (1964). Imprinting and short-term retention. *Brit. J. Psychol.*, **55**, 181–187.

SMITH, F. V. (1960). Towards a definition of the stimulus situation for the approach response of the domestic chick. *Anim. Behav.*, **8**, 197–200.

(1962). Perceptual aspects of imprinting. *Symp. zoo. Soc. Lond.*, *No. 8*, 171–191.

SMITH, F. V. & BIRD, M. W. (1963). Varying effectiveness of distant intermittent stimuli for the approach response in the domestic chick. *Anim. Behav.*, **11**, 57–61.

SMITH, F. V. & HOYES, P. A. (1961). Properties of the visual stimuli for the approach response in the domestic chick. *Anim. Behav.*, **9**, 159–166.

SPALDING, D. A. (1873). Instinct, with original observations on young animals. *Macmillan's Magazine*, **27**, 282–293. Reprinted in 1954 in *Brit. J. anim. Behav.*, **2**, 2–11.

SPITZ, R. A. & WOLFE, K. M. (1946). The smiling response: a contribution to the ontogenesis of social relations. *Genetic. Psychol. Monogr.*, **34**, 57–125.

STANLEY, W. C., CORNWELL, A. C., POGGIANI, C. & TRATTNER, A. (1963). Conditioning in the neonatal puppy. *J. comp. physiol. Psychol.*, **56**, 211–214.

STEVEN, D. M. (1955). Transference of 'imprinting' in a wild gosling. *Brit. J. anim. Behav.*, **3**, 14–16.

STONE, C. P. (1929a). The age factor in animal learning. I. Rats in the problem box and the maze. *Genet. Psychol. Monogr.*, **5**, 1–130.

(1929b). The age factor in animal learning. II. Rats in multiple light discrimination box and a different maze. *Genet. Psychol. Monogr.*, **6**, 125–202.

TAYLOR, K. F. & SLUCKIN, W. (1964a). Flocking of domestic chicks. *Nature*, **201**, 108–109.

TAYLOR, K. F. & SLUCKIN, W. (1964b). An experiment in tactile imprinting. *Bull. Brit. psychol. Soc.*, **17**, No. 54, 10A.

THOMPSON, W. R. & HERON, W. (1954a). The effect of restricting early experience on the problem-solving capacity of dogs. *Canad. J. Psychol.*, **8**, 17–31.

(1954b). The effect of early restriction on activity in dogs. *J. comp. physiol. Psychol.*, **47**, 77–82.

THOMPSON, W. R. & MELZACK, R. (1956). Early environment. *Sci. Amer.*, **194**, 38–42.

THORPE, W. H. (1944). Some problems of animal learning. *Proc. Linn. Soc. Lond.*, **156**, 70–83.

(1951). The learning abilities of birds; Part 2. *Ibis*, **93**, 252–296.

(1954). The process of song-learning in the chaffinch as studied by means of the sound spectrograph. *Nature*, **173**, 465–569.

(1955). The nature and significance of imprinting. *Brit. J. anim. Behav.*, **3**, 121.

(1956). *Learning and Instinct in Animals*. London: Methuen. Second edition: 1963.

(1961). Sensitive periods in the learning of animals and men: a study of imprinting with special reference to the induction of cyclic behaviour. In: Thorpe, W. H. and Zangwill, O. L. (Eds.). *Current Problems in Animal Behaviour*. Cambridge: C.U.P.

TINBERGEN, N. (1951). *The Study of Instinct*. Oxford: Clarendon Press.

(1958). *Curious Naturalists*. London: Country Life.

VERPLANCK, W. S. (1957). A glossary of some terms used in the objective science of behavior. *Psychol. Rev. Suppl.*, **64**, No. 6, Part 2.

VINCE, M. A. (1958). 'String-pulling' in birds. 2. Differences related to age in greenfinches, chaffinches and canaries. *Anim. Behav.*, **6**, 53–59.

(1959). Effects of age and experience on the establishment of internal inhibition in finches. *Brit. J. Psychol.*, **50**, 136–144.

(1960). Developmental changes in responsiveness in the great tit. *Behaviour*, **15**, 219–243.

(1961). Developmental changes in learning capacity. In: Thorpe, W. H. and Zangwill, O. L. (Eds.). *Current Problems in Animal Behaviour*. Cambridge: C.U.P.

WALK, R. D. (1960). Responses of dark- and light-reared rats to stimulus change. *J. comp. physiol. Psychol.*, **53**, 609–611.

WALK, R. D., GIBSON, E. J., PICK, H. L. JR. & TIGHE, T. J. (1959). The effectiveness of prolonged exposure to cutouts vs. painted patterns for facilitation of discrimination. *J. comp. physiol. Psychol.*, **52**, 519–521.

WALLER, P. F. & WALLER, M. B. (1963). Some relationships between early experience and later social behavior in ducklings. *Behavior*, **20**, 343–363.

WEIDMANN, U. (1956). Some experiments on the following and flocking reaction of mallard ducklings. *Brit. J. anim. Behav.*, **4**, 78–79.

(1958) Verhaltensstudien an der Stockente. II. Versuche zur Auslösung und Prägung der Nachfolge- und Anschlussreaction. *Z. Tierpsychol.*, **15**, 277–300.

WHITMAN, C. O. (1919). The behavior of pigeons. In: Carr, H. A. (Ed.). *Orthogenetic Evolution of Pigeons, Vol. 3*. Washington: Carnegie Institution.

WOOD-GUSH, D. G. M. (1950). The effect of experience on the mating behaviour of the domestic cock. *Anim. Behav.*, **6**, 68–71.

YARROW, L. J. (1961). Maternal deprivation: toward an empirical and conceptual re-evaluation. *Psychol. Bull.*, **58**, 459–490.

# NAME INDEX

# SUBJECT INDEX